The Perfect Pair

The Dolphin Trilogy

for our fantastic Mum and Dad

Barbara and Ron Holroyd

with all our love

The Perfect Pair: Shards from the Mirror – a story that will forever change hearts and minds.

When reading the first two books of *The Perfect Pair Dolphin Trilogy*, you will experience a range of emotions: sadness, anger, frustration, sympathy and complete and utter disgust. You will even learn something about the dolphin psyche.

But nothing will prepare you for this final instalment – it will tear out your heart and leave you emotionally spent.

This ex-dolphin trainer's mind-blowing testimony is one of the best anti-captivity books I have ever read. It takes you on a journey, from the excitement of a young man securing his dream job to his life of inner turmoil and self-destruction. The reader experiences his battle to protect his beloved dolphins against sickness, injury, death and even management sabotage.

In a short time he comes to understand just how ugly the captive cetacean business really is, and how nothing, but *nothing*, is allowed to interfere with company profits.

No matter what, the show must go on!

So this broken trainer makes the decision to walk away from the industry he once loved, never to return.

I stand in awe of David Capello's courage, dedication and determination. The majesty of his love and his ability to connect so deeply with his dolphins is nothing short of incredible. One can only imagine what mental and emotional anguish he must have suffered when he chose to leave his beloved dolphins behind, knowing what their fate would ultimately be. This trainer, like many before him, realised that he could no longer be a part of this vile business.

Once you have read the final book of the trilogy, you will fully understand why this story has been subject to so much resistance. Those *big* businessmen behind the captive industry are fully exposed for the greedy, repulsive, negligent 'PARASITES IN SUITS' that they truly are – so much so that the names of people and places have had to be changed. However, as the authors have pointed out, the names of the dolphins and other animals remain unchanged.

Bravo to David and Tracy Holroyd for having the passion, courage and determination to push this story out! Books such as these, along with the testament of ex-trainers, graphically illustrate what happens behind closed doors. Exposing the dirty rotten secrets of the captive industry is key to emptying the tanks and destroying the business of cetacean exploitation throughout the world, whether it be in the form of a dolphinarium or a 'swim with' programme.

I am an avid cetacean advocate, and love all animals. It's my hope and dream that one day this ugly industry will be a thing of the past, and that no more dolphins and whales will be forced to endure the pain and suffering of being ripped from their families to be locked away in tiny concrete pools, then forced to perform tricks to survive.

The captive industry claims to educate – but there is *nothing* educational about captivity. Real education is teaching *people* – and especially *children* – that captivity is *wrong*. Real education is seeing these majestic, sentient beings in their natural habitat, *not* visiting them in a dolphinarium where *nothing* is natural.

I pray that all cetaceans be left to live their life free in the ocean as God intended. I, for one, will continue to fight on their behalf, and do whatever possible to save them.

Shelley Anne Guinn
Co-founder of the Facebook page *Swim for Freedom – Marine*
Mammal Advocates

★★★

"Treat a dog like a man and you will have a noble animal ..."

After reading this book, this quotation could, I believe, apply equally to dolphins and the training 'industry'. The book is well written; the story flies along quickly and simply, and its message is stark and uncompromising.

... treat him like a dog and you will have a poor beast that knows far more than you because he can understand you but you can't always understand him."

Tom Whiting, FCIIA

★★★

This important trilogy takes the reader on a roller-coaster ride – from the excitement of working with such wonderful marine mammals to the harsh reality of their existence in captivity.

This final part of *The Perfect Pair Dolphin Trilogy – Shards from the Mirror –* will demonstrate to the discerning reader just why cetaceans should *not* be kept in captivity ... especially not for entertainment, which is so cruel.

Captivity simply *cannot* provide a suitable environment for these intelligent animals, who are in many ways one of our closest cousins in terms of communication and behavioural sophistication. In my opinion, even with the finest pool facilities, this is still the case. However, add inadequate facilities and poor management to the equation, and the captives do not last long.

Obviously, to protect the innocent (and, for legal reasons, the guilty too!), this story is written as a 'Faction' – a fusion of fact with some fiction – leaving the reader to discern where fact ends and fiction begins.

Personally, from my own experience as a zoo and wildlife vet, the facts outlined in this story when dealing with the corporate bodies behind animal entertainment are sadly all too familiar. Corporate accountants should *never* be allowed to overrule the welfare needs of animals used in entertainment, yet the financing and maintenance of even minimum welfare standards are only just beginning to be enforced.

As a young zoo vet, I was actively involved in the zoo reform movement to change zoo *raison d'être* from 'Animal Entertainment/Attractions' to 'Conservation, Education and Welfare' – a message that is lost on wild animal circuses and the many aquaria and animal attractions that are now appearing throughout the developing world.

So *please* don't make them profitable by visiting them.

My heart goes out to poor David – the only one who really had any understanding of the behavioural and health needs of the dolphins he loved so much. He was their only human advocate as most couldn't, or *wouldn't*, understand them ... and *the worst* simply didn't care.

By publishing this wonderfully-written and important testimony, let us all hope that the key message – that cetaceans should *not* be made to perform for public entertainment – finally gets through.

It is extremely sad that Capello's psychic/empathic ability to communicate so effectively with cetaceans was lost to the world. However, I fully understand and support his moral dilemma and, as you will see, he did everything he could to help them.

My experience in the corporate-controlled zoo world was similar and just as traumatic, and I, too, left to become an independent adviser with the aim of promoting improved zoo and wildlife welfare. David Capello's brave testimony has certainly pricked my conscience, spurring me to one day tell *my* story.

I hope that other trainers who have experienced this close *connection* with their dolphins and whales will contact the authors to explore this fascinating ability, which could lead to a whole new understanding of cetacean behaviour.

In summary, if you care about dolphins and whales, *don't* support those who hunt them, whether their aim be to kill them, or to condemn them to a slow, torturous death in the captive 'entertainment' industry.

If you want real dolphin entertainment, take a boat trip and visit them in their natural home – the sea!

Further comment: David Capello … well done, sir, you have my respect and gratitude on behalf of dolphins and cetaceans held in captivity everywhere!

Dr Simon JR Adams, BSc (Hons), BVMS, MRCVS
Independent Zoo and Wildlife Veterinary Adviser

★★★

The unmissable conclusion to this compelling trilogy. The stakes are raised and emotions intensify as our hero battles the corporate machine for the sake of his dolphin charges. We plunge from the ecstasy of the 'shadow ballet' into the depths of corruption in a heartrending narrative that grips until the final page. The mirror may be smashed but what it shows us is a deeply moving and beautifully written meditation on the nature of love.

Dr Ursula Hurley, Fellow of the Higher Education Academy, MA Cantab, MA Lancaster
Senior Lecturer, English and Creative Writing

***

This third and final volume in *The Perfect Pair Dolphin Trilogy* skilfully knits together all the pieces from the previous two volumes, providing an ending to those stories started in them. This volume is quite dark – necessarily so – as there is little by way of humour or light-heartedness to be found in the ultimate demise of some of the planet's most beautiful and wonderful creatures.

Here, we witness our hero, David Capello, once again locking horns with those charged with managing the enterprise and maximising revenue. His nemesis, Backhouse – excelling in the role of bad guy, demon and all round shyster – is at the heart of all the ills that plague David and his waterborne charges, his actions and decisions having far-reaching and devastating consequences for all concerned.

It is not before time that the truth was revealed about how whales and dolphins are exploited in pursuit of money, their welfare coming a very poor second where profits are concerned. All costs cut to the bone, everything down to a price rather than up to a quality; the two sides of *this particular* coin being mutually exclusive. The animals and their trainers pay the ultimate cost of entertaining Joe Public – the trainer in this case being David Capello, whose anguish is palpable as his journey approaches its climax.

Although the events described in this story happened more than forty years ago, the problems that beset the authors from day one demonstrate the ongoing power of those responsible for these enterprises: opportunities to publish via mainstream agents and publishing houses closed, obstacles placed at every turn and – most surprising of all – lack of support from globally-recognised animal welfare charities. The captive industry does not want the public to know how these animals – blessed with a permanent smile – are treated in order to provide the paying public with twenty or thirty minutes of entertainment up to ten times a day.

Permanent dolphinariums are bad enough, with the lifespan of their captives severely curtailed due to lives spent swimming in a chemical soup. (Imagine the impact on your lifespan if all you had to drink was the water from your local swimming baths.) However, conditions in travelling shows are much, much worse, with a massive mortality rate amongst the performers – dolphins rarely lasting more than one season … if they're lucky.

I am particularly saddened to see major tour operators touting whale and dolphin shows as part of the 'entertainment' purchased with package holidays, and I would implore each and every one of you, dear readers, to never set foot in any arena where cetaceans are being exploited in this way — for without your attendance, they could not exist.

I, for one, never will.

Vincent Meehan, CMIOSH, GIFE
Ex-trainer/presenter

★★★

It's true — fact stranger and more brutal than fiction! If you care about our fellow inhabitants on this earth, *The Perfect Pair: Shards from the Mirror* is a must-read book.

Please, please READ, and let's hope we learn to give cetaceans — and *all* our beautiful life-sharing friends — the respect and care they truly deserve. Perhaps, then, we can eliminate any future repetition of these horrendous events.

Spirit Guide Cara
Psychic to the Stars

★★★

We've had gangster dolphins, kinky dolphins, stinky penguins and a stubborn sea lion, all seen through the eyes and mind of trainer, David Capello, in two fishy blockbusters exposing the insane world of the aquatic circus. Now comes the third, and final, part of what is essentially a tragic trilogy of the human-led fall of the two captive dolphins, Duchess and Herb'e.

During the first two 'faction' novels, Capello has been using his unique psychic bond to entice Duchess and Herb'e to become the greatest show dolphins in Britain, despite the cruelty and profit-hungry corporates all around him. Now he's aiming for *The Perfect Pair* to do a synced forward somersault — yet another metaphor for the hoops Capello has to jump through as he tries to maintain the welfare of mammals that should really be swimming free in an ocean somewhere.

His predicament, previously kept numb by Valium, erupts into the open amidst a management that registers only the cash tills of the paying public … and none of the pain of the captured dolphins in its charge. The show pool that Capello calls his 'enchanted mirror' holds a multitude of horrors that the audience never sees.

'They're prisoners of the mirror …' he exclaims, '… What a rotten, horrible, horrible existence … And for what? Their smile, their generous smile – a feature that remains fixed even when they cry. What a terrible price to pay for simply looking happy …'

And for those dolphins who won't, or can't, perform … there may be murder afoot; rather than the slow, sad, toxic death applauded by unknowing families who come to watch the aquatic circus.

This third blockbuster, *Shards from the Mirror*, is again beautifully written by authors, David C Holroyd and Tracy J Holroyd, with page-turning anticipation of what psychic jokes and treats the dolphins have in store for us – and, in turn, what neglect we humans can spew onto such intelligent creatures.

All through *The Perfect Pair Dolphin Trilogy*, the message has been clear – 'You wouldn't go and see a lion or tiger perform, so why go and see a performing dolphin and perpetuate a cruel trade?' The idea is so controversial that these books have been almost suppressed by the big publishers – but to anyone with a soul it's common sense. A campaign that's time has come …

Stephen Kingston
Editor, *Salford Star*

★★★

A truly remarkable story – the completion of *The Perfect Pair Dolphin Trilogy* – a masterpiece.

David Capello's psychic experience of transposition will be of particular interest to quantum physicists who are investigating the phenomenon, adding to our knowledge of the mysteries of the Universe.

Sheila Reeves Rigby
Author of *Life's Mysteries – Your Key to Understanding*

★★★

The mirror really turns vile in this third and final part of David and Tracy's story, which fully exposes the horrific circumstances which the devoted young Capello has to experience those in his trust endure. Our trainer is driven to the very end of his sanity, trying to protect and care for his loved Atlanteans. Masterfully described by the authors David and Tracy, we discover just how strong his psychic link has become and the tragic consequences of decisions taken solely based on money. I felt that I was living the experiences with him as I read every word of this story with no doubt of the clarity of its message. Again uniquely written – it is the story that had to be told!

Ian Rothwell
Award-winning Radio Presenter

★★★

And so we come to the final chapter in *The Perfect Pair Dolphin Trilogy* by authors David and Tracy Holroyd – and what an ending! *The Enchanted Mirror* has been well and truly shattered.

Anyone who has read the first two books (and you should have done) will be familiar with dolphin trainer David Capello's amazing psychic bond with his beloved Atlanteans and the love that they share.

Once again, we see David's struggle with his arch nemesis, Backhouse, who finally reveals his true colours. The glitz and glamour of the world of dolphinariums is fully exposed for what it truly is, an unforgiving money-making machine with no regard for these beautiful creatures when the show must go on at all costs.

Let's face it, who doesn't love a dolphin? Cute, intelligent creatures with permanently smiling faces – yet we know little of what they have to endure.

Money is all that matters as corners are cut: dolphins being forced to live and swim in a chemical fog that is supposed to pass for water, fed unimaginable slops and, when they have outlived their usefulness, simply abandoned and left to die.

It is obvious when reading this book that David Capello has witnessed first-hand the terrible ordeals that these poor creatures are forced to endure in the name of profit, and if you have ever contemplated visiting a dolphinarium, then after reading this story you should feel ashamed of yourself.

The first two books introduce us to the loveable Duchess, Herb'e, Baby, Scouse, Bonnie, Clyde, Bubbles, Stumpy, Eccles and Twinkle, and they are great reads, as we learn more and more about the bond between the trainer and his charges.

Initially the reader is not made aware of what is going on in the background; all seems sweetness and light … well almost.

The mood slowly darkens, as does Capello's health – both mental and physical – as the truth begins to slowly unravel and he is forced to face his demons.

The psychic bond that he shares with his Atlanteans is torn asunder as they feel betrayed by their treatment and let down by David.

I daren't spoil the ending, but *please* I urge you to not only finish the book, but also to take time to take in what you have read.

I guarantee that this book will shake all your pre-conceived ideas of dolphinariums with the nice image of well-fed dolphins happily performing for your entertainment.

This is a 'warts and all' exposé, so don't be expecting whimsy or light-heartedness, because you will be disappointed.

It's little wonder that certain authorities have tried to have this book blacklisted, but the truth *must* be told, and it's told here in no uncertain manner.

A five star must-read!

Tony Flynn
@ SalfordOnline.com

★★★

Brilliant book, written with deep feeling and psychic awareness. This final book can stand alone, but is the excellent finale of a 'must read' trilogy.

I felt at one with David Capello, as the truth about dolphinariums unfolded with increasingly intense emotion, deep love and psychic connection. I read with admiration, sadness and relief for both David and the dolphins.

Jill Bowyer
Award-winning Radio Presenter

The Perfect Pair

Shards From the Mirror

David C Holroyd

and

Tracy J Holroyd

Matador
9 Priory Business Park,
Wistow Road, Kibworth Beauchamp,
Leicestershire. LE8 0RX
Tel: 0116 279 2299
Email: books@troubador.co.uk
Web: www.troubador.co.uk/matador
Twitter: @matadorbooks

ISBN 978 1785890 963 (Paperback)
ISBN 978 1785890 970 (Hardback)

British Library Cataloguing in Publication Data.
A catalogue record for this book is available from the British Library.

Printed and bound in the UK by TJ International, Padstow, Cornwall

Matador is an imprint of Troubador Publishing Ltd

The Perfect Pair
Shards from the Mirror

By William Roache, MBE

After the first few sentences, we are brilliantly drawn into the world of David and his beloved dolphins, feeling the stifling atmosphere and actually smelling the dolphinarium. It is hard to believe that it has taken almost six years to write *The Perfect Pair Dolphin Trilogy*, from *The Enchanted Mirror*, through *The Mirror Cracks*, to *Shards from the Mirror*. How wonderfully this story has been told, in such a compelling way that each book was read in almost one sitting.

The message is clear and powerful. Humanity has reached a stage where it is intolerant of the abuse and ill treatment of animals, especially in the world of entertainment. And David, who should have been praised and respected for his ability to communicate with his beloved dolphins, was treated with equal cruelty by the corporate bodies that slavishly used him and his charges as money-making objects.

David was an idealistic young man with dreams of greatness for his dolphins, but instead found himself in the lonely position of fighting not just for their well-being, but also for their very lives.

It is easy to understand why *Shards from the Mirror* took so long to write. You feel that this book is actually wrenched from David's heart, and that must have been a painful process. But the result is a deeply moving and fascinating story that will stay with you for a long time. Hopefully it will lead to the end of the barbaric treatment of these magnificent animals, allowing them to be treated with the love and respect they deserve.

NOTES FROM THE AUTHORS

Finally, I can get my life back!

The book you are now holding is the culmination of nearly six years' blood, sweat and tears. In bringing you this trilogy, my sister and I have quite literally had to fight every inch of the way. So to all you fantastic people who have supported us throughout this mammoth task, a heartfelt thank you.

Most of you will already know that *The Perfect Pair Dolphin Trilogy* is in fact a true story written under the 'Fiction' banner to avoid the threat of legal action. But despite this - and our efforts to maintain the anonymity of the central characters - the book blocking has been nothing short of scandalous.

So where do I start?

When Tracy and I first embarked on this project, we were told to expect trouble, that there would be those who would try to stop us. What we couldn't have envisaged, however, was just how many there would be or how hard they would try. And no wonder - researching the Capello story has been like opening a proverbial can of worms.

We've been forced to deal with fearful media agents, an obstructive journalist, a pro-captivity ex-handler and a vindictive charity that's gone out of its way to prevent *you* reading this book. To say nothing of previously supportive media that we can only assume have been intimidated into pulling their backing. I say 'assume' because neither the newspaper nor the magazine in question will offer any explanation.

But the biggest disappointment of all has to be those global charities that purport to protect the world's beautiful cetaceans — something our supporters should consider when said charities appeal for their hard-earned cash. For us, as animal advocates, dealing with them has been soul-destroying. So we've taken the unprecedented step of listing every single one of them in the back of this book.

And, with that final act of defiance, it's rant over and back to what's most important - the story.

I honestly feel that *Shards from the Mirror* is our best writing to date; that we've managed to capture in detail the strengths and frailties of the troubled trainer Capello. To achieve this, Tracy and I have enhanced the groundbreaking techniques introduced in the first two books - a vital innovation that grants the reader insight into Capello's tormented obsession. This technique also allows us to illustrate more clearly the quagmire of cruelty and greed prevalent in this loathsome industry.

But my final comments have to be for my sister, Tracy, who abandoned her successful career as a children's writer to help me publish this exposé. As authors, we have sacrificed much to bring you this insider knowledge – an awareness that will help you to decide whether the global aqua-circus is truly worthy of your support.

They say that people power can quite literally change the world – something I passionately believe. But, as always, the choice is down to the individual … and the individual alone.

Thanks for listening.

David C Holroyd
Member of the Society of Authors

Well, what can I say? At last, this amazing story is finished, actually *finished* – something my mind is still having trouble accepting. This project has been, without doubt, the toughest I have ever undertaken; a Herculean task, made even more arduous by the vindictive charities that have done their utmost to stop *you* reading this story.

And what a story it is!

It's far, far more than just an exposé, as you will appreciate in the reading. So for those of you who possess a logical disposition, a friendly word of warning: you are about to have your cages well and truly rattled. However, before you pass judgment, please, *please* remember that the tale of *The Perfect Pair* is a true story that struck fear into the captive dolphin industry over four decades ago. And, if our current trials are anything to go by, little has changed.

Why?

Firstly, this tale illustrates just how emotionally intelligent a dolphin can be. Further, it demonstrates the ease with which human and Atlantean minds can bond; a phenomenon of which the captive cetacean industry would much rather have you blissfully unaware.

So it was with Capello and his charges.

During the telling of this story, we did not intend to drag our readers into the realms of fantasy – yet events chronicled within these pages sometimes appear to take us there. Nevertheless, it's worth remembering that no one connected to this young trainer could ever offer a logical explanation for the astonishing things they witnessed. Many of you will question the validity of Capello's psychic ability, yet the celebrity vet, Philip Haynes, was so convinced that he actually talked about it during a TV interview.

However, *your* interpretation, as always, must be your own.

So on behalf of Duchess, Herb'e, Baby, Scouse, Bonnie, Clyde, Bubbles, Stumpy, Eccles, Twinkle, Blodwyn and Ramu, could I please ask one last favour?

Think of all those ill-fated Atlanteans now languishing in concrete boxes around the world, and *give* them a voice. Tell family, friends and neighbours. Accost people in the streets and shout from the rooftops. The world needs to know of their torment.

We've done our bit. Now the rest is up to you.

Tracy J Holroyd, Cert Ed, BA(Hons)
Member of the Society of Authors

ACKNOWLEDGMENTS

We would like to thank the following people for all their help and support during the writing and production of this book:

Our fantastic Mum and Dad, Barbara and Ron Holroyd, who endured so much neglect during the writing of this trilogy. Please forgive!

Marion Ibbotson and Paul Goodier, who passionately shared our dreams, but never saw our project completed. We will always remember your love and support.

William Roache, MBE, whose unfailing support and excellent forewords have helped propel us towards a wider audience.

Dr Simon JR Adams, BSc (Hons), BVMS, MRCVS, Independent Zoo and Wildlife Veterinary Adviser, for his continued encouragement, advice and endorsements. Also, for his unwavering belief in our project and his efforts to spread the word.

Dr Ursula Hurley, Fellow of the Higher Education Academy, MA Cantab, MA Lancaster, Senior Lecturer, English and Creative Writing, for her ongoing support and fabulous endorsements.

Sheila Reeves Rigby, Author, for her continuing support throughout this project, along with her wonderful endorsements and valued feedback.

Stephen Kingston, Editor, *Salford Star*, for his witty, insightful endorsements and terrific press coverage. (www.salfordstar.com)

Vincent Meehan, CMIOSH, GIFE, Ex-trainer/presenter for having the courage to add his voice to ours in defence of our beautiful Atlanteans. Your excellent endorsement, friendship and support throughout this entire project have given us strength.

Tom Whiting for his friendship and support under difficult circumstances. Also, for his feedback and excellent endorsement. Many thanks.

Spirit Guide Cara, Psychic to the Stars, for her boundless enthusiasm, friendship, spiritual guidance and insightful endorsements.

Jill Bowyer for her endorsements and fun radio interviews — but especially for her friendship.

Ian Rothwell for his endorsements, thought-provoking radio interviews and continued support and encouragement.

Tony Flynn of *SalfordOnline.com* for his continuing support, powerful endorsement and excellent media coverage.

Shelley Anne Guinn, Co-founder of the Facebook page *Swim for Freedom - Marine Mammal Advocates*, for her support, touching endorsement and unwavering advocacy for our world's beautiful cetaceans.

Don and Irene Campbell for their ever-cheerful support and Don's amazing photographs. Without you, much of the important photographic evidence would have been lost.

Shirley Swaine — a good friend and a talented photographer whose photographs helped to validate this story. Also, a big thank you to her father, Edgar Swaine, for his phenomenal close-ups. We couldn't have done it without you!

Our beloved cousin, Antony J Reid of Reid Design & Illustration (www.reiddesign.co.uk) for his advice and digital origination of the book's graphic layout. Thank you for all your work.

Rodney James Charman for spending so much time and energy promoting *The Perfect Pair Dolphin Trilogy* throughout the Land of Smiles …Thailand. David's promise to you gave him purpose. He, too, likes a man who keeps his word. A big, big thank you.

Paul Strachan and Peter Malhotra of *Pattaya Mail* and Pattaya Mail TV. Thank you for your support and excellent media coverage.

Nick Pendrell and Dave D from *Good Morning Pattaya*, Pattaya Channel TV for your support and excellent TV coverage.

The Rotary Club Eastern Seaboard Pattaya RCES – Thailand and all its members. Especially Rodney James Charman, Jan Abbink, Brian George Alexander and Nigel Quennell.

To all at *Pattaya Trader Magazine* for their reviews and unwavering support.

Ben Reeves, Journalist, for his insightful and forthright reviews.

Anthony Tommo Thomas for his friendship and support, and for everything he does for our planet's precious animals.

Eleanor Walk, David Mather and Peter Robinson of *Salford Folk* (Salford City Radio) for their staunch support and insightful interview.

Salford City Radio's Sufiya Rehman for her fun interviews.

Lynne Booth, our adopted sis, who has worked tirelessly to promote this story. A huge, huge thank you for everything. Also, her son, Darryl Riley, who has followed his mother's orders with grace and humour!

Rosemary and Chris Lovett for their continuing friendship, support and invaluable introduction to Dr Simon JR Adams.

Barbara and Vince Meehan for their unfailing friendship.

Frank Jones – passionate in his defence of animals, and fearless in his defence of our story. Thank you, Frank.

Terence David Joy, landlord of Park Inn, Swinton, along with all his customers, for keeping the faith! Your support has been fantastic!

Lenny Bowers, barman extraordinaire, for his sunny disposition and outstanding service.

Roger Collier for his friendship and fabulous support throughout David's obsession.

Julie Barton for tirelessly promoting our story – a huge, huge thank you.

Sandra Chapman, Pam Kaye and Anita Mikolaites for their enthusiasm and friendship.

June Jones for her loyalty and friendship to Mum and Dad.

Finally, the many friends and family members, too numerous to mention, who have supported and encouraged us. Thank you all: we love you.

CREDITS

Cover photograph of *The Perfect Pair*: Don Campbell.

Cover design: Antony J Reid and David C Holroyd.

Cover font: *The Perfect Pair* – created and designed by David C Holroyd.

Digital origination of the book's graphic layout and artwork: Antony J Reid of Reid Design & Illustration. www.reiddesign.co.uk

Original photographs: Don Campbell, Shirley Swaine and Edgar Swaine.

Digital restoration of original photographs: Tracy J Holroyd.

Line drawings (badge artwork): David C Holroyd.

There was a boy, a very strange, enchanted boy …
This he said to me,
"The greatest thing you'll ever learn is just to love and be loved in return."

(From *Nature Boy* by Eden Ahbez)

1

Whoa! Fantastic … absolutely bloody fantastic!

I thrust my face headlong into Thor's embrace, sieving his northern tang through bared teeth. The rushing wind lashed at the dolphinarium balcony, whipping my cheeks and stealing my breath …

… an explosive elixir courtesy of the Norse thunder god.

Then, in a flash, it hit me: something was different – there was a subtle change in the air. Although still sharp, the gale's rough caress was lacking its needle sting, and no matter how devious the ice lord might be, he could no longer conceal his secret. The god of thunder's emissary had exposed winter's impending demise, heralding a new ruler – spring!

Even the penetrating cold striking through the balcony's metal barrier couldn't dampen my relief. Soon, the maze of twisted figures peppering Hendle's landscape would soften as they slipped once more into the lush, green coats that would signal the beginning of a new show season.

It seemed hard to believe that, in just over two months, this vantage point would bear witness to the annual pilgrimage of thousands of true believers – misguided worshippers all eager to step inside my cathedral.

The Hendle pool – what a truly magnificent sight!

It reminded me of a Biblical ark, its impressive structure towering imperiously over all it surveyed. A purpose-built mantrap to tempt the public from near and far …

… inviting … oh so inviting …

If only they knew the truth.

If only they knew what really went on behind the closed doors of a dolphinarium – the true cost of their fleeting entertainment …

If only they knew …

But they didn't know … didn't *want* to know …

But I knew … yes, *I* knew …

Still, I couldn't help but wonder: even if they were aware, would it actually make a difference? Would the masses stop coming? Or would they nonchalantly shrug their shoulders and hide behind their apathy?

Somehow, I think they'd still come.

Yeah, I'm sure they'd still come …

… after all, everyone wants to see a dolphin.

2

Standing on this balcony brought back memories – memories of when I was a kid, playing king of the castle. What a sight! You could literally see for miles and miles.

A wave of dizziness hit me, and my grip on the metal barrier instinctively tightened. From this precarious perch, the shops and kiosks looked like miniature boxes cowering in the shadow of their lord and master. The only other building of any size was the park restaurant directly to my right, or "Monkey Eden", as I liked to call it. Just one look at that place never failed to muster a smile, especially when I visualised all those marauding baboons scampering across the parking area to raid its bins.

It struck me as strange how something as mundane as a building could conjure such emotive memories. That especially held true when I looked at Kiddies' Kreche, down to my left …

… Captain … my little elephant friend … how I missed him.

Then, just beyond Kiddies' Kreche was Sea Lion Lake – a picturesque legacy fortuitously bestowed on the park by nature. A watery expanse that, if rumours were true, housed an old and dear friend of mine – a wide-eyed amigo I'd thought never to hear of again.

Talk about a blast from the past! Would you believe?

Bobby!

3

Deliver Us from Bobby! The first trial by ordeal to be foisted on me by my money-fixated employers. A trial that came in the shape of a large and problematic Californian sea lion – deemed by Management as too vicious to live, but too valuable to kill.

Bobby, surreptitiously whisked away from City Zoo, where he faced certain execution, to be concealed in an old, disused swimming pool situated in the middle of nowhere.

North Liston – a sleepy, Shire mining village that you'd struggle to find on the map.

Again, I had to smile – what a wake-up call they got!

I could still vividly recall the flash of rage in Bobby's huge green eyes as he bared his teeth and homed in on that foul-mouthed miner. Still see him unceremoniously galloping along the pavement, hell-bent on shredding his petrified quarry – totally and utterly oblivious to his audience of open-mouthed motorists.

What a culture shock …

… to witness a live sea lion tearing down the middle of an unobtrusive village road, frantically pursued by a long-haired kid brandishing a deck scrubber.

Bizarre – totally bizarre. You literally couldn't make it up!

As for Bobby himself, as well as my first big adventure, he was my first true friend, which is why it was so sad that we'd parted under such a cloud.

It was painful to recall the abject look of betrayal he'd given me after the zoo handlers had beaten him from the pool and into his crate. How he'd stuck his nose in the air before shuffling unceremoniously around to shun me. Heartbreaking, because he'd never realised just how lucky he'd actually been. If we'd failed to catch him, he would have been darted – something he could never have survived.

Yes, there was no doubt that Bobby was one lucky sea lion, because on that day, he'd effectively cheated death for a second time ...

... an otherwise tragic event that I would have been forced to witness.

Good old Bobby – talk about leading a charmed life!

Crazy how fate played games with people's lives – I'd thought Bobby long gone, yet, unbeknown to me, the lucky sod had been my next door neighbour for the past two years, living in what could only be described as "sea lion paradise".

Unbelievable – yet another uncanny twist of fate!

❧ 4 ❧

"Blimey, it's getting a bit fresh up here – this wind is really starting to bite!"

I grimaced. Maybe my earlier assessment of spring spreading its wings was a bit premature – that is, unless spring was wearing an overcoat. Still, a few more minutes up here shouldn't do any harm. After all, there was nothing like a long, sharp blast of good old northern air – especially if you were in the market for a dose of double pneumonia!

Tilting back my head, I inhaled deeply, assimilating the wind's unique bouquet – an intoxicating ambience unpolluted by the tinge of salt to which I'd become so accustomed.

Invigorating – absolutely invigorating!

As the gusts continued to pummel my face, my gaze again channelled back to sea lion paradise … and thoughts of Bobby.

An awful lot of water had passed under the bridge since last I'd seen my troublesome friend, those early days at North Liston now just a blur – much like my past two years here at Hendle. I'd certainly had to grow up fast, because all I'd seemingly done since then was lurch from one disaster to another. Typical of a business that promoted the survival of the fittest.

Talk about echoes of the past … I could still hear my old mentor's words ringing in my ears: "Remember, dolphinariums don't just break dolphins, they break people too."

How right he was! Gerry Mansell – I wondered what he was doing now. It seemed like only yesterday when the men in suits were hailing him a king. "Europe's finest trainer!" they'd proclaimed.

What a turn-around!

Still, that had been an age ago – long before Backhouse had arrived on the scene to stab him in the back.

But Gerry hadn't been the only victim of Backhouse's treachery. There'd been my good friend Vance Martin, the deliciously pretty Sally Summers and God knows how many others who'd unintentionally got in his way.

Tommy Backhouse – my esteemed general manager!

What a charm offensive he'd staged on first joining the Company, wooing us all with his sweetness and light, whilst all the time deviously plotting to get rid of anyone whom he deemed dangerous to his ambition. And, like fools, we'd all stood around and let him do it.

Yeah, he'd certainly done a number on us – and he'd worked overtime on our Company bigwig, Rogers. A man who, even now, remained hopelessly smitten by his golden boy – so much so that he just couldn't see which one of them was actually pulling the strings.

As for me, I still found it hard to understand how a man who'd never actually trained a dolphin could have become so powerful within the dolphin world. I had to hand it to him – Backhouse had succeeded in conning the leaders of an international conglomerate into believing him to be an expert in dolphin welfare. It beggared belief!

I remembered how Vance had once referred to him as a snake in the grass. Well, my old friend was bang on there …

… if anyone had had him sussed, it was Vance.

❦ 5 ❧

A further complication: I was patently aware that I had become the major topic of conversation within the hallowed halls of Head Office. I'd heard on the grapevine that some in the Company hierarchy were now viewing me as a loose cannon – a plant no doubt courtesy of Backhouse. They were openly questioning how someone barely out of his teens could hold such sway over thousands of pounds worth of Company assets – namely, dolphins.

How had this happened? More importantly, how had this been allowed to happen? Awkward questions directed at an old-style executive who wasn't used to having to explain himself – Rogers.

For me, these murmurings were a new and extremely worrying development. For the first time, Head Office was no longer viewing my achievements with pride, but with alarm – perhaps even fear – no doubt compounded by reports of my recent battle against Valium addiction; a hard-won victory that had clearly left some of the men in suits rattled.

It seemed that my list of enemies was growing daily.

So, overall, my outlook appeared bleak – especially with an ever more powerful Backhouse on hand to fan the flames.

The only way I could see of forestalling the inevitable was to present the Company with something huge … something exceptional … something that would render me untouchable …

Only the double forward somersault could fit that bill. Only the final piece of the shadow ballet could keep Backhouse and his supporters off my back.

It seemed bizarre that, despite all my past glories, my entire career now hinged on the training of just one trick – one very special trick – a trick that would propel *The Perfect Pair* to instant stardom and make me – their trainer – indispensable.

That Duchess and Herb'e would work for no one else but me was common knowledge. However, it was only just emerging that they were not alone in their ferocious loyalty. It was shared by a certain blind dolphin now exiled at West Coast – a dolphin who had point-blank refused to work since his enforced deportation …

… Scouse.

A further indication of the Company's growing unease was its apparent reluctance to send me to West Coast to bring Scouse back online – although this may also have had something to do with my row with Clive Rothwell. After the devastating commandeering of my tiny duo – a crime that still haunted me – I'd publicly accused him and his staff of gross incompetence, embarrassing everyone involved.

Yes, no doubt about it, things were looking decidedly black.

I'd got enemies at West Coast …

I'd got enemies at Head Office …

I'd alienated Tony Forrester, the vet, with my blackmailing tactics …

And, if all that wasn't bad enough, I had Backhouse constantly grinding me down …

… to say nothing of poor Scouse who was again paying the price for my insubordination.

Could it get any worse?

Probably.

Anyway, enough fresh air for one day, I had work to do …

… I had a somersault to train.

{ 6 }

Just what is a double forward somersault?

It's a dream turned into a nightmare … an obsession that won't let go … a burning ambition – all-consuming – constantly taunting when I'm awake, totally draining when I'm asleep.

Yet I have to have it … I have to have it …

I can only liken it to the replaying of a video clip over and over. The obsessive scrutiny of every last detail – every minute pixel of every individual frame – as they spin through the air: Duchess and Herb'e, bodies joined like two aeroplanes trailing a single smoke plume that patterns the sky.

What is a double forward somersault?

It's a curse.

A bewitchment.

My curse.

My bewitchment.

Yet I have to have it … I have to have it …

❧ 7 ❧

The next few weeks demonstrated how my cold turkey assault against my Valium addiction had paid dividends: I felt reborn, my mind clear of the drug-induced fog that had for so long plagued me.

However, I had less success with Herb'e. My mischievous dolphin was fervently holding out for a full reintroduction of the somersault training – his beloved fish bonanza. He was stuck in a typical dolphin mind-set and my so-called man-to-man talk had only hardened his resolve.

We were now locked in a stalemate.

In a fit of pique, I petulantly packed away all my somersault props – a blunt message intended to convey my frustration to my wayward star.

"That's it, Herb'e! You've had your lot! No more somersault training… in fact, no more nothing! I've had enough!"

And so it began – our winter of discontent. The cold shoulder. The big freeze. The Herb'e-Capello stand-off.

However, in contrast to the icy atmosphere inside the dolphinarium, the world beyond had begun to thaw, inviting spring to make her long overdue appearance.

Keen to take advantage, I embarked on a thorough spring clean with Dan and Carol. It was then that I noticed how tatty our show props had become, so decided to drive into Hendle village to buy materials with which to carry out a colourful renovation.

As I walked along the high street past the local post office, I found myself weaving through a lively crowd of senior citizens queuing for their pensions.

The milder weather had encouraged a good turnout, and they milled together excitedly, swapping the reservoir of gossip they'd stored throughout the harsh winter months.

Amongst them, I couldn't help but notice a rather glamorous lady flirting outrageously with a throng of male admirers. I stood on the sidewalk, transfixed: I'd seen this lady before … but where?

Aware of my gaze, she sharply turned to eyeball me, before breaking into a beaming smile. "Why, it's David … David Capello! Hello … how are you?"

"No way," I gasped. "It can't be … it can't be *Miss Crouch* … can it!?"

I couldn't believe it! Could this stylish, self-assured woman really be my timid old landlady from Munster Mansion?

Indeed it could!

Amazing – it was like looking at a different person. Gone were those long, wispy whiskers, that timid droop and the drab, unkempt hair. Instead, I was now facing a seemingly much taller lady sporting full makeup and a modern hairdo – a far cry from the downtrodden creature I'd once known.

"I still can't believe it!" I gabbled, finding it hard to hide my delight. "Gosh, Miss Crouch, I hardly recognised you! You look great … absolutely fantastic! How are you doing … and how's your mum?"

Still smiling, she girlishly tossed back her head. "Oh, unfortunately, dear Mother passed away some sixteen months ago. It was a very sad time – but, after all, she was ninety-seven, so she'd had a good innings." She seemed buoyantly unperturbed – relieved, even. "Nevertheless, David, I've a lot to be thankful for. In fact, I'm a very lucky lady, because – unbeknown to me – it turns out that Mother was quite wealthy." She paused, eyes twinkling mischievously, before leaning over to whisper, "In fact, to be perfectly honest, David, very, *very* wealthy."

I couldn't help but beam a knowing grin, which she immediately reciprocated.

"Good for you, Miss Crouch!"

We continued to move along the queue, chatting and laughing until the dark shadows of the post office entrance threatened to consume us. Then, saying my goodbyes, I left her – with an upbeat skip in my step.

I literally couldn't have been happier.

Good for Miss Crouch! At last she had the chance to live her life as she pleased, and although it might have come a little late in the day, it was definitely a case of better late than never!

❧ 8 ❧

My Perfect Pair's logbooks didn't make inspiring reading, my abysmal failure with the forward somersault etched in black and white for all to see. For me, an utterly unacceptable situation.

It was blatantly obvious that I still had a lot of soul-searching to do if I were to stand any chance of reaching my goal. The question was, just where should I start?

My ultra-clever Herb'e was, without doubt, the number one player in the somersault, because he was already holding its image in his mind – something with which he impishly taunted me. This mischievous Atlantean simply loved to play mind games.

However, even Herb'e couldn't be satisfied with our current impasse, as it was benefiting neither one of us. So, perhaps the difficulty wasn't down to him alone – perhaps Duchess had a role in this too.

Much as I loved my princess, there was no doubt that when it came to cool logic, Herb'e had her beaten hands down. He was nowhere near as sensitive as she was, so rarely allowed emotional matters to cloud his vision. On the other hand, Duchess had shown a marked behavioural change when I'd started going out with Carol – a betrayal she'd never forgotten, borne out by the fact that she still wouldn't allow Carol into the pool.

So, could the problem be jealousy on Duchess' part? An emotion that might equally explain Herb'e's uncompromising stance towards me – after all, in his eyes, I might well be the rival suitor trying to steal away his girl, in which case I'd been wrong about his apparent emotional indifference all along.

There were so many permutations to consider, bringing to mind the saying: "Oh, what a tangled web we weave ..." An adage that magnificently illustrated the crazy, mixed-up world the three of us actually inhabited – we were quite literally a psychiatrist's dream!

But, joking apart, I felt that this analysis of the situation had brought me one step closer to truly understanding why things hadn't been working out.

One: Herb'e was jealous of *me* and angry with Duchess because she loved me.

Two: Duchess was jealous of Carol and angry with *me* because she felt betrayed.

Three: Herb'e was angry with *me* for showing favouritism towards Duchess by giving her a solo trick, which was the very reason he had specifically targeted her highball in the first place. He was showing me, in his own unique way, that he too demanded a trick of his own: the forward somersault – the jewel in the crown. Sadly, the one thing I couldn't allow him to have – well, not as a solo, anyway.

Which brought me to reason number four: Duchess was angry with Herb'e for repeatedly sabotaging her highball, and angry with *me* for not disciplining him.

Meanwhile, I'd been drifting through Valium City in zombie-like oblivion, completely unaware of the drama unfolding around me.

What a summing-up!

Yet, as incredible as it might seem, it all made perfect sense.

Our failure had been down to letting our personal hang-ups get in the way. Little wonder I'd been contemplating jacking it all in. I'd begun to fear that I was living in a lunatic asylum; yet, in truth, it was anything but.

There was indeed method behind the madness.

❦ 9 ❧

First show of the day and Duchess and Herb'e were going through one of their customary marital tiffs, both tolerating rather than enjoying each other's company. There was no doubt that things between them had never been the same since the introduction of the now-mothballed somersault training – something that was clearly continuing to cause a rift.

The audience was treated to a twenty-minute barrage of snapping, shoving and nose-butting until we reached Duchess' highball – the point where Herb'e would try to steal her thunder.

Conscious of the skirmish to come, I nervously signalled Duchess to begin her run-up.

But, at that point, something magical happened …

Although my eyes were focussed on Duchess' form, her image never reached my consciousness. It was as if her run-up had triggered a mental shift, much like the sudden switching of a TV channel, causing my forward vision to blur and snap inwards …

… the substitution of physical reality by a waking dream …

… a vision *not* of Duchess' highball, but of Herb'e's forward somersault.

But was the picture inside my head of my own making, or was it a plant by Herb'e?

I suspected the latter, because this storming of my psyche had now become a regular occurrence at this point in the show.

This couldn't be just coincidence. Someone was seriously messing with my head – priming me, fine-tuning me.

As Duchess sped around the pool, Herb'e did not disappoint. He again darted across her path, making it impossible for her to complete her build-up.

"Ohhh … great, Herb'e, just great! At it again, are we?" I growled. *"Yet another highball ruined!"*

My unrepentant double-chinned rebel gave me a long tongue pull as he swaggered cockily by.

I had to smile – albeit through clenched teeth. Even though Herb'e had sabotaged Duchess' highball, I found it impossible to stay mad at him. Observing Herb'e's behaviour was like stepping back into the school playground, reminding me of the status you could achieve by possessing that ultra-rare collector's card – the card all your rivals craved. The card that Herb'e now nursed in his psyche.

And boy, didn't he just know it!

"Don't get upset, beautiful. Herb'e's just showing off."

My clumsy attempt to placate Duchess didn't go down well, and the water bubbled with her remonstrations.

"Don't get upset? Showing off? What do you mean, showing off?"

I'd just dropped myself in it …

"He ruins my trick every time, and all you *can do is stand there smirking. Well, I'm sick of him, and I'm sick of you!"*

… sinking deeper into the mire.

"Okay, okay, I'll get it sorted, Duch, I promise …"

As usual, I tried to pacify her by rewarding a double feed, but although she accepted the bribe, she was still far from happy.

For Duchess, this wasn't about extra fish – it was about fair play.

❧ 10 ❧

As the week progressed, Herb'e gleefully persisted in sabotaging Duchess' highball – and with his every foray, the magnificent vision of the somersault grew sharper in my mind. It was as if Herb'e were refining my receiver whilst at the same time building my expectation.

I sensed beneath his cocky façade a fast-mounting desire to cash-in his prize card.

I was definitely getting near, begging the question: could this sudden mood change be the light at the end of the tunnel?

Not for the first time, I found myself smiling down at him from the poolside, purposely trying to shut him out and hide in a silent *connection*.

Dan looked at me, baffled. "What's so funny? We've just lost the highball again."

I didn't reply – Dan couldn't possibly understand the significance of what was happening, and it would take too long to explain. We may have lost another highball, but I felt deep down that we'd gained so much more.

My dream of the somersault had just taken a huge leap forward. My beloved adversary was most definitely cracking, and our marathon stand-off was entering its final straight.

Herb'e was on the verge of revealing his secret.

❦ 11 ❧

It's been over a week now, and still no somersault.

Worse, Herb'e's continuing to cause pandemonium with Duchess' highball, desperate to force a reinstatement of his fish bonanza.

Well, no chance – he's already shown too much of his hand for that.

"Talk about Duchess having had enough, Herb'e ... I've had enough. I don't care about your crummy somersault anymore. In fact, I'm fed up to the back teeth with it ..."

His garbled comeback punches a hole through my entire being – a last ditch attempt to impose his will.

"What do you mean, crummy somersault? You want it ... I know you want it ... you've always wanted it. It's your *dream, and you'll never let go!"*

Well, can't argue with him there – even so, I've got to at least *try* to mask my feelings.

"Like I said, Herb'e, I don't need your rotten, lousy somersault. You can stick it!"

He understood that all right – he's just smashed his tail on the water.

"Throwing a wobbler won't do you any good, either. Like I said, I don't need your poxy somersault."

(God, hide your face and cringe, Capello – you're turning into a right liar.)

Another tail smash reverberates throughout the dolphinarium.

He's trying to get to me. Can't afford to lose my rag. Got to play it cool. The last thing we need is a slanging match.

So, the big question is, what's he gonna do next?

What a stupid, stupid question – as if I didn't know …

"Yeah, yeah, Herb'e, that's right, take it out on poor Duchess. Ruin her highball again."

He taunts me with another vision.

"I told you before … stick your somersault! All you're doing by spoiling the highball is giving Duchess extra fish and making her fat."

A double-double tail smash …

… he didn't like that either!

Well, tough!

Now's the time to twist the knife – lay it on thick with the whistle and feeds, make as much fuss of Duchess as I can.

"There you go, girl – double feeds again today. Great, innit?"

A triple-triple tail smash …

… Herb'e's going ballistic, absolutely ballistic!

Ignore him, Capello – just ignore him.

My errant thought hits a raw spot, and he shakes his head furiously before taking the route of shame to the sulking corner of the pool.

So much for ignoring him. Damn! How many times do I need reminding that the *connection* works both ways?

"Yeah, that's right, Herb'e. Stay there and pull your face for as long as you like, because no one's bothered."

Now I'm the one who's being ignored.

But, thankfully, the show goes on, because Herb'e's disappearing act brings a smug Duchess swimming into my arms.

"About time you sorted him out!"

"How right you are, how right you are … my beautiful, beautiful girl …"

Cupping my hands around her scrumptious face, I give her a big fat kiss …

… and wonder if he's watching?

"Yeah, Herb'e's not good like you, is he, Duchess? He's a bad boy … a bad, bad boy …"

But, bad boy or not, he's at the end of his tether …

… he's about to spill the beans.

Come on, my son … Somersault, here we come!

❦ 12 ❦

It's coming ... I know that it's coming ...

There goes the telephone ringing mercilessly off the wall. It's the park management tipping us off that three coachloads of punters have arrived wanting to book a show, meaning we're expecting a large audience. Unusual so early in the season, so I need to be on top of my game.

They've scheduled the show for within the next hour, giving me just enough time to consult my enchanted mirror.

As always, the first to greet me is Duchess, flashing those lovely blue eyes.

"Hello, beautiful, everything okay?"

She doesn't say anything, but just transmits that warm feeling of contentment.

"You lovely, lovely girl. Now, where's that mischievous partner of yours?"

Herb'e rushes to the stage.

I give him a friendly nod, but don't get involved in any conversation. Still playing it cool ...

... yet I sense something – something magical. There's a sudden rush of expectation; a feeling I can't shake – don't want to shake – and if *I* can feel it, so can *he*.

I'm really buzzing – light-headed, having trouble catching my breath.

Come on, Capello, get a grip ... you've got to stay calm.

I can hardly wait for this show to start. The anticipation is making me nauseous – something I haven't felt in a long time. Is it a *connection* kicking in? I'm not sure ... just feeling giddy.

It's coming ... I know that it's coming ... I've never been so sure.

God, I feel sharp today, feel like *I* could make a forward somersault, never mind Herb'e. It's like stepping back in time. Gone is the Valium-induced fog in which I've hidden for so long. The radio is full on, transmitting and receiving with a diamond-cut clarity …

It's *him* – it has to be him. It's Herb'e doing some last-minute fine-tuning. Whoa … and is it working …

… it's like being born again!

I dither backstage expectantly, listening to the muffled conversations of the punters as they take their seats. Not long now – five minutes, maybe ten, before the show starts. Not long now …

It's coming … I know that it's coming …

As the music fades in the auditorium, Dan waits in the wings. As usual, he gives me a nod and a smile, but I'm so deep in thought that I don't reciprocate. That's rude, so I look again, but Dan's already gone …

… on stage and halfway through his opening spiel.

The show has already begun. Somewhere along the line, I've just lost five minutes of my life.

It's coming … I know that it's coming …

Butterflies … butterflies in my stomach. It's crazy – I haven't felt butterflies for ages …

It's coming … I know that it's coming …

A surge of loud applause. That's my cue. At last, I'm on stage.

Throughout the show, I try to stay focussed, but I'm having difficulty. My concentration keeps faltering, so I'm only halfway in the loop. But it's not my fault – it's … *his*. Something keeps drawing me back to my right hand side, drawing me back to Herb'e.

"David, what's wrong with you?"

Duchess rebukes me – and she has every right.

"I know, Duch, I'm sorry."

She doesn't reply, but gives me a rare, stern stare – a sure sign that I've got to pull my socks up.

I'm holding my concentration better now, because I don't want my diva telling me off again. But I'm in an impossible position: I'm being bombarded by a vision – a vision of the somersault.

It's coming … I know that it's coming …

An age has passed and we've only reached the halfway point of the show. Time has slowed to a crawl.

Dan is chatting to the audience, giving the three of us a well-deserved rest.

God, the last thing I need right now is a rest!

Herb'e's still not speaking, but continues to draw me in, sapping my will. I'm in a daze, finding him hard to resist – in fact, I'm finding him impossible to resist.

It's coming … I know that it's coming …

"What's wrong with you, David? Never mind him! Concentrate!"

Duchess is beginning to lose her rag, and who can blame her? Come on, Capello, keep it together – you have a show to do!

At last, at long last, the performance moves on. Just two more tricks, then it's Duchess' highball – the moment of truth.

I can hardly breathe …

… it's coming … I know that it's coming …

Duchess' highball is the catalyst …

… I know it is …

… I'm sure it is.

Dan's already into the verbal build-up introducing one of the highest jumps in the country, cleverly geeing up the crowd, raising their expectations…

… yet I hardly hear him.

I feel nauseous … feel like I'm about to throw up.

It's coming … I know that it's coming …

Suddenly, everything goes into slow motion.

Somewhere in the distance, the echo of Dan's commentary dissolves into a slur, slowing like a record player running out of power – slowing … slowing … slowing …

It's coming … I know that it's coming …

I feel drunk …

… my eyelids are heavy and I'm running on autopilot.

I give the highball signal and Duchess turns to begin her run-up.

It's as if I'm dreaming. Time has grown sluggish. I can't feel the stage beneath my feet – can't even sense Duchess – only that surge of power emanating from my right hand side.

My shared *connection* with Duchess has been compromised …

… there's no room for her …

… only room for *him*.

I'm trying to concentrate, trying to accommodate Duchess, but Herb'e's forcibly prising open the door to my mind and, even with all my weight behind it, I'm powerless to stop him. He's like a juggernaut, his sheer strength of will forging a supercharged *connection* – a power play that I am unable to resist. He's rushing in like a raging tsunami, smashing everything in his path.

It's coming … I know that it's coming …

He demands my assistance, and he demands it now! He can't do this on his own.

This is *his* time. This is *his* moment of greatness, and I need to give him my undivided attention …

… but our bond corrupts as another door crashes open …

… Duchess … it's Duchess.

"He's done it again! Look, he's done it again! He's ruined my trick!"

Mentally, I'm being ripped apart – Duchess on one side, Herb'e on the other. I'm in a no-win situation.

Duchess isn't just angry, she's furious.

"Calm down, Duch, calm down …"

She's not having it – she just keeps on shouting.

"What's wrong with you, David, what's wrong with you? Didn't you hear me? He's ruined my trick!"

She's screaming uncontrollably, but I can't answer. I must push her out. I've got only a tiny window in time to do what I have to do, and I can't allow any interference.

There's room for only one, and that's Herb'e.

It's coming … I know that it's coming …

From the corner of my eye, I spy a blur below the waterline …

… Herb'e … picking up speed.

I hold my breath in anticipation …

… it's coming … I just know that it's coming …

… it's going to happen, and it's going to happen now!

The image of the somersault is branded onto my psyche. I've imagined this moment a billion times – ever since first becoming a trainer.

An eruption of a thousand diamonds as Herb'e rockets from the water, cold air smashing into his body.

Everything is in super slow-mo – so much so that I can actually see each individual water droplet rolling down his sleek form to fall into space.

I'm an artist moulding clay, meticulously creating my masterpiece – but I can only do so much from here …

… I *need* to be with him …

… I need to *feel* him …

… I need to *be* him …

… and Herb'e knows it!

Muscles aching, tearing, morphing – every fibre of my body merging with his, transmuting into the dolphin form …

On stage, a stranger now stands in my place, and Herb'e wears my psyche like an overcoat.

I'm in the air …

… *we* are in the air …

We force our chin into our neck …

We lower our head, arcing our body like a crescent moon …

Forward, forward, forward – sheer momentum spinning us into the somersault.

Our silver grey form revolves like a Catherine wheel, sparking fireflies under the overhead spotlights.

Round, round, round – a full one and a half revolutions before spearing the liquid mirror.

The fingers of the clock stop.

There's no sound.

No echo of applause.

Nothing.

Only silence.

Standing outside time – in another dimension – I am alone once more, staring at a video freeze-frame.

Everything is crystalized – nothing allowed to move until I press the start button in my mind …

I wait, savouring the vision …

What an image …

… what an absolutely magnificent image!

Instinctively, my other self detonates the whistle, shattering the air with decibels that bounce from wall to wall – an audio signature tearing the fabric of time.

"What ARE you doing? Look what he's done to my trick!"

Duchess bursts into my head, literally going crazy. But no sooner does she arrive than she begins to fade, pushed out – steamrolled – by Herb'e's sheer, uncontrollable, triumphant laughter.

Herb'e's reminding me that there's only room for one – only room for him. And who can blame him? Today, he has joined the ranks of the elite.

"Was that good? Was that good or what?"

He's hooting, and no wonder! If anyone has a right to hoot, he has.

"You old rascal! I knew you could do it … I just knew! How long have you known?"

He won't answer – doesn't have to answer – just continues his noisy celebrations.

God, it's bedlam! I'm being pushed from pillar to post. Between his excited cries and Duchess' torrent of complaints, I literally don't know where I'm up to. It's like a football match – a chaotic three-way *connection* propelling us onto another plane.

Poor Dan, he thinks I've gone loopy, as does an audience that – for me – disappeared at least thirty minutes ago. All those disappointed punters who waited for a jump that never came, a highball that never materialised.

Makes me wonder just how many of them managed to assimilate what they got in its place? How many recognised that flash of inspirational brilliance?

Twenty …? Ten …? Five …?

Probably not even five, because what they witnessed took mere seconds in real time.

They feel cheated, but I don't care. All I care about is us: Herb'e and me. We're the lucky ones. We are the ones who have blasted to another level – far, far from the madding crowd.

Although the same can't be said for poor Dan, who seems just as confused as our bemused audience. He's gazing at me with concern, waiting for an explanation. Well, he's not gonna get one – well, not right now, anyway! Like everybody else, he'll just have to wait until I make touchdown, which – from the way I'm feeling – isn't going to be any time soon.

I want to stay a while with Herb'e, share in his triumph. After all, this moment is down to him – and *only* him.

Today, Herb'e has given me the platform to launch my dream. This magnificent dolphin has pointed the way to the greatest routine of them all.

"You clever, clever boy, Herb'e! Enjoy!"

❧ 13 ❧

I'm still giddy with excitement, still finding it hard to take in. To think that I've seen it, actually seen it – a dream come true.

Crash! Bang! Wallop! The kitchen door bursts open.

"Will someone please tell me what's just happened out there?"

Dan.

"One minute I'm expecting a highball, then next minute, you're telling me to announce Britain's first ever forward somersault … Forward somersault? I didn't see a forward somersault!"

Is he kidding or what?

"How do you mean, you didn't see it?" I groan, throwing him an exasperated look. "How could you *not* have seen it? You were right there on stage with me. I mean, you *must* have seen it!"

"Well, I didn't! All I saw was Duchess giving you grief over losing her highball, then you smothering Herb'e with fish."

Crash! Bang! Wallop! There goes that infernal door again.

"What's going on? What's with all the noisy whistles?"

Great! That's all I need – Carol to swell the ranks of the unbelievers.

"The somersault … the *forward somersault*! Didn't you see it?"

Carol gives me a blank stare before throwing Dan a bemused look. "No, I didn't see anything. I was too busy focussing on Duchess' highball. It was only when you went ballistic with your whistle that I realised something must've happened."

God – unbelievable! The first forward somersault performed in Britain, and no one's clocked it!

"Well, for what it's worth, you've both missed something incredible – fantastic, in fact."

Drooping jaws – they put me in mind of a Venus flytrap.

"The forward somersault …" I wail. "I'm talking about Herb'e's forward somersault!" I throw them another exasperated look.

Silence. Utter silence.

(Is there anybody out there?)

"I don't believe it! Are you both half-asleep or what?"

Infuriating – still no visible signs of life.

Now it's my turn to throw a strop.

"Well, I've got more to do than hang around here all day discussing what you two did or didn't see. For starters, Duch and Herb'e – I need to try and put things right between them, 'cause right now Duchess is *not* a happy bunny."

Not a happy bunny at all!

14

First job was to get Duchess and Herb'e back together again, so we decided to challenge them to a friendly game of football – Team Duchess and Herb'e versus Team Dan and Me.

Although this ploy could hardly be deemed rocket science, a bit of *them* against *us* always went a long way towards reuniting our feuding couple – vital if we were to progress to the next level of somersault training. Unfortunately, this playtime invitation didn't extend to Carol, as my green-eyed Duchess still wouldn't allow her in the water.

Once my *Perfect Pair* had finished giving us a good kicking, Dan and Carol packed up for the night, leaving me to log Herb'e's flash of brilliance in the diaries.

Even though Herb'e's somersault had been a bit rough around the edges, this first foray had set us firmly on the road to achieving that most coveted prize: the shadow ballet. To perfect this routine, all I needed now was patience, a clear head and lots and lots of quality time – commodities all readily at hand, so long as Backhouse didn't get back from Welby any time soon. Without doubt, my general manager's presence at Hendle would shatter any creative momentum between my dolphins and me …

… so it was fingers well and truly crossed.

❦ 15 ❧

Just how had I managed to reach this stage?

In truth, all my early training had achieved was to get two dolphins leaping over a hurdle to hit a couple of beach balls. Hardly a somersault.

Yet, amazingly, from these relatively simple beginnings, Herb'e had managed to glean the greatest trick of them all. This posed two important questions: how had he known what was required of him, and for how long?

The answer to the first had to be, our psychic bond, because without our shared vision, he could never have achieved this somersault. As for how long he'd held the mental picture? That was anyone's guess.

Smiling, I ruffled my hair. I couldn't help but wonder just which one of us here had actually been jumping through hoops?

Judging by the evidence, most probably me.

Nonetheless, I'd managed to claw back the trust of my Atlanteans and regain my enchanted mirror – all thanks to the gift of resolve bestowed on me one winter's night by an angel shouldering a ticket machine …

… a kindness I'd never forget for as long as I lived.

As always, before turning out the light to leave for home, I couldn't resist one last peep into the pool.

"Mirror, mirror on the wall, who is the cleverest of them all?"

A sharp, watery snort gave me a final dismissal.

"For God's sake, go home, David!"

Yeah, Herb'e – it's most definitely Herb'e!

❦ 16 ❧

A full week had gone by since Herb'e's forward somersault and the pool was still buzzing. Already his fabulous one and a half turns had progressed into an even more spectacular two.

Only one problem – and it was a big one – he was still insisting on performing his extravaganza during what should have been Duchess' highball – something that was infuriating her.

Duchess felt that Herb'e was being rewarded for what she deemed to be bad behaviour. I could certainly see her point, because not only was Herb'e sabotaging her highball, he was also dictating the show agenda – something I'd never tolerated in the past.

Rightly or wrongly, in my eagerness to secure Herb'e's somersault, I'd placated his impish ego by lapsing discipline, a concession that my diva Duch was unwilling to endorse.

So, for me, it was again back to my enchanted mirror for another heart-to-heart.

⟨ 17 ⟩

Smelly and Worse had been particularly productive overnight, meaning our customary morning clean-up took a little longer than usual. However, even the stinky leftovers of our grumpy penguins couldn't dampen my mood. So, once everything was shipshape, I cheerfully prepared to embark on my planned pep talk with my two stars.

Kneeling at the pool's edge, I called Duchess and Herb'e into the stage so that I could look them directly in the eyes. Being up-close and personal like this recalled those early days at North Liston when I'd worked belly-down on the training platform, so this was as much for my benefit as it was for theirs.

"Hello, people, time for a team talk …"

My *Perfect Pair*, bobbing less than two feet away, eagerly rested their chins on the poolside to listen.

"Right, Herb'e, you first …"

Nodding, he flashed me a large, toothy grin.

"From now on, if you continue to perform the forward somersault during Duchess' highball, you won't get fed! It's as simple as that. In fact, I won't even blow the whistle … I'll totally ignore you!"

Cocking his head to one side, he continued to listen intently.

"You know full well that you and Duchess are supposed to be a team, so performing the somersault solo is not acceptable. Either teach Duchess how to do it, or it's finished. It's up to you."

Herb'e's open-mouthed smile dissolved as he realised that he'd just been on the receiving end of a good ticking off. Meanwhile, Duchess smirked smugly, clearly relishing her partner's discomfort.

Turning to her, I continued.

"As for you, Duchess, instead of constantly moaning about Herb'e giving you a hard time, do something about it!"

Realising that she too was receiving a reprimand, Duchess jerked her chin from the stage.

"I mean it, Duch – this can't go on. I'll carry on feeding you when he ruins your highball, but only for the next two days. After that, you've had it!"

Silently bobbing in the water, my two Atlanteans stared at me, wide-eyed.

"It's no good looking at me like that. It's up to you two now. Either sort yourselves out or I'll drop both tricks from the show. You, Herb'e, will lose your precious forward somersault and you, Duchess, will lose your solo highball. I mean it ... I'm not willing to put up with this anymore."

Duchess and Herb'e gaped at each other in disbelief before turning to swim from the stage like two scolded schoolchildren. It was clear that both had a lot of soul-searching to do.

Gingerly hauling myself from aching knees, I suddenly became aware of Dan grinning at me from the kitchen doorway, obviously amused by the frantic head nodding and face pulling that always accompanied my non-verbal rebukes.

"Well, that told them! They certainly know the score now, don't they?" he announced drolly. Laughing, he thrust a piece of paper into my hand. "Here, Dave, this is for you ... I couldn't resist."

It was a poem.

It seemed that Dan was finding the psychic interaction between me and my dolphins so fascinating that he'd been compelled to put pen to paper ...

... I guess once an academic, always an academic.

I was no connoisseur when it came to poetry, but I had to admit, I thought it wasn't half bad.

LIVING (THROUGH A BAD DAY) WITH DOLPHINS by DC

A bad day. What did I do? What did I forget to say?
The shows were up to standard. We didn't hear the applause.
No-one was supposed to notice when she refused to feed,
And in tight-lipped insolence jumped higher than the compère's

Praises. Then he, reckless villain, belly-flopped precisely
Two inches from the stage. I stood dripping with helpless rage,
Smiling through clenched teeth at the unjust laughter and applause.
Slighted, rejected and soaked right through,
What did I say? What did I forget to do?

Banished from my thoughts: in disgrace. Someone else gave the feeds.
As I write up my embarrassment in the logbook, brush
Fish-scales from my hair, put away the litter of the day,
Mentally run through a thousand possible disasters
That never happen, turn the key; I know they've been watching me.
I take three uncertain paces towards my car. I stop.
I listen to their silence accusing me: then return
Against my will, to the pool without switching on the light.
Out of the darkness comes a furious snort. I say, "Goodnight!"

Spot on, Dan – love it to bits!

❦ 18 ❧

A further two weeks of hard training and Duchess was finally getting to grips with the forward somersault. It seemed that my team talk had reaped rich rewards. Fearing the loss of his beloved trick, Herb'e had begrudgingly shared his secret with Duchess, and although the somersault still wasn't up to show standard, it was now only a matter of time.

It was amazing to think that in just a few short weeks I would at last reach my goal, achieve what I'd once feared unachievable: the greatest show routine of them all, the fabulous shadow ballet. The very thought of it whipped my breath away: Duchess and Herb'e finally recognised as the world's finest …

… the greatest show dolphins ever …

… the legendary *Perfect Pair*.

It just didn't get any better.

As a bonus, I knew that Philip, our playboy vet – now an international ambassador in his field – would waste little time in spreading our news globally – a success that would have the whole dolphin world at our feet. It beggared belief!

Yet for me, it all felt strangely surreal, my excitement tempered by uncertainty. The completion of the shadow ballet would be the culmination of all my hopes and dreams, the quenching of my obsession. But once achieved, then what? What would the three of us do next? Would this be an end to the glory road? Or could there be more?

I just didn't know. However, these were concerns for another day – after all, we weren't there yet, and I couldn't allow any negativity to dampen my dream.

My *Perfect Pair* and I had all but won our epic race against time – not to mention those sinister figures harbouring hidden agendas.

I felt proud, very proud. At last, Duchess and Herb'e – *my* Duchess and Herb'e – finally recognised as the mythical *Perfect Pair*.

⟨ 19 ⟩

Even during the happy times, there was never any shortage of storm clouds lurking on the horizon – as Carol was about to remind me.

"I hate to put a dampener on things, David, but I've got something I must tell you. I've been offered a job at a marine studies centre on the south coast – something I seriously have to consider."

A proverbial bolt from the blue.

As my feisty colleague broke the news, I noticed that she seemed uncharacteristically subdued – in fact, almost apologetic – so much so that I instinctively knew she'd already accepted.

Biting my lip, I turned my face aside. "It's certainly a tempting offer, Carol, and one that might never come again." Then, with a sigh of resignation, I lifted my head and forced a smile – after all, it was pointless swimming against the tide. "Yeah ... in fact, it's more than tempting, it's fantastic. If I were you, I'd jump at it."

Carol's relief was plainly evident. "Thanks for being so supportive, David. I knew you'd understand. It's my dream job and, to be honest, I'd already made my decision. But, then, you probably knew that ..."

I didn't comment – just gave her a reassuring nod. "Well, I guess that's settled, then. When were you thinking of leaving? We're short-staffed, so I could do with at least two weeks' grace to sort out your replacement."

"Two weeks it is, then."

A quick peck on the cheek sealed the deal – and that, as they say, was that. Short and sweet. No long, poignant farewells – just "So long, David". Carol certainly wasn't the kind of girl to let the grass grow, which was probably why she'd so fascinated me in the first place. Even so, she'd hit me with a double-whammy, as I wasn't only losing a valued colleague, but also a dear friend.

But the bad news didn't end there. Carol's imminent departure meant that I'd now have no option but to inform Backhouse how we'd soon be one member of staff down – news that would undoubtedly bring him scurrying back to Hendle. The last thing I wanted.

To add to my woes, despite two backwashes a day, the pool water was deteriorating morbidly – a fact I'd conveniently chosen to overlook in my all-consuming pursuit of the somersault. However, ignoring it was no longer an option. The water was dying fast. In fact, it was actually beginning to smell – yet another delightful snippet to report to Backhouse.

"Dammit!"

❦ 20 ❧

Begrudgingly, I telephoned Welby – only to find Backhouse in uncharacteristically good humour. "No worries, David," he assured me cheerfully, "do as many backwashes as you think fit. I'm more than happy to leave the management of Hendle in your capable hands…"

Was I hearing him correctly? Did he actually say he was *happy* to leave the management of Hendle in *my* hands? If so, this was a refreshing – if not perplexing – change of heart, especially in light of his previous history. Paradoxically, no matter how welcome this carefree response might be, it couldn't fail but trigger alarm bells. This was certainly *not* the Backhouse of old. Why was my illustrious general manager suddenly being so accommodating? Was I missing something or what?

His sudden turnabout, along with his more than obvious desire to remain at Welby, got me thinking. Maybe, just maybe, he'd managed to find himself a girlfriend. After all, stranger things had happened.

Either way, I did *not* intend to look this gift horse in the mouth, as it would gain me precious Backhouse-free time to perfect my somersault.

"Glory road, here we come!"

⟨ 21 ⟩

A fortnight later, my two magnificent superstars were rolling through the air with breathtaking precision. Duchess and Herb'e's somersault was now fine-tuned and ready for inclusion in their show routine. The fabulous shadow ballet was at last complete.

However, news of this success triggered the response I'd been dreading: Backhouse, prompted by the allure of this unique series of tricks, was already speeding his way back to Hendle. His reason? The publicity generated by my dream team's achievement needed proper management.

Although to the bosses at Head Office his reasoning might sound plausible, he wasn't fooling me. Duchess and Herb'e's feats were now unparalleled in the dolphin world – something my general manager knew all too well.

For him, this wasn't about managing the shadow ballet …

… it was about claiming it.

❧ 22 ❧

Backhouse's arrival resulted in the now customary summons to his office. We didn't bother exchanging pleasantries, but instead got directly down to business.

"Within the next month, a specialist team will be coming to Hendle to perform a complete renovation of the filters," he announced. "Head Office doesn't want a repeat of last year's fiasco when we had to dump the pool during high season."

His reference to last year's "fiasco" – which had been entirely down to him – couldn't help but generate a warm feeling of satisfaction, along with an almost uncontrollable urge to say "I told you so".

Instead, I made do with a diplomatic: "Well, it's about time the Company finally got round to sorting those filters. They've been nothing but a nightmare."

Taking care to maintain his air of superiority, Backhouse nodded coolly. "Furthermore, in celebration of Duchess and Herb'e's double forward somersault, I have arranged for a camera crew to visit the dolphinarium and film the show in its entirety … once the somersault is perfected, of course."

"Wow, a film crew?" I gasped. "That's fantastic – what an honour!"

Then he dropped the bombshell.

"During the filming of this show, under no circumstances must either you or Dan engage in any conversation with the camera crew. They'll have enough on their plates without you two pestering them. All communication must go through me and me alone. Do I make myself clear?"

I frowned. He'd made himself perfectly clear.

Was it my imagination, or was he deliberately pushing me out? What harm could there possibly be in talking to a camera crew? After all, surely they'd want to speak to the show's trainer, if only out of interest. That is, of course, unless he'd neglected to tell them that I *was* the trainer … in which case, just who *was* taking the credit for this show?

Despite my reservations, this wasn't the time to lay down the law. Now was the perfect moment to exploit my success with Duchess and Herb'e, and I needed to keep Backhouse on side.

"Well, Tommy, as I've already said, the filming of Duchess and Herb'e's show is a big honour – a real big honour. And since it's largely down to me, how about the Company giving me that pay rise I've been after? Let's face it, I've more than earned it."

Backhouse visibly stiffened. "You already know Company policy on this matter: under no circumstances shall one member of staff be deemed superior to another – not even you. Presenter pay is now standardised and there can be no exceptions."

Presenter? I was getting just about sick and tired of hearing him describe me as a presenter, especially in light of all I'd accomplished.

"Are you serious or what? I've given this Company the best show in Europe, yet you still have the audacity to refer to me as a presenter. God, Tommy, you've got some nerve!"

Backhouse leapt to his feet. "Like I said, I won't break Company policy for anyone – especially not you! Now, if you've quite finished, I have work to do …"

Moments later, the dolphinarium was reverberating to the slamming door that, of late, always accompanied my exit from his office.

Backhouse was again refusing to acknowledge my achievements – deliberately pushing me into the shadows – and despite all my efforts to convince myself that I didn't need his recognition, I was absolutely devastated.

Forever the schemer, my general manager had at last acquired the ultimate meal ticket; a publicity machine fit to feed his insatiable ego: Duchess and Herb'e – *my* Duchess and Herb'e. And, with this achieved, the last thing he wanted was me around to rain on his parade.

I was now surplus to requirements …

… surplus to requirements and elevated to the top of the expendable list.

❦ 23 ❧

A sticky week followed, the atmosphere laced with a deep-rooted malevolence, the toxic by-product of two men who literally couldn't stand the sight of each other.

For me, Backhouse had turned into a long-festering boil aching to be lanced and – general manager or not – a reckoning was coming, and coming fast.

However, this sudden upsurge in testosterone-driven posturing had an unexpectedly poignant consequence: during this time, Carol quietly and unobtrusively slipped out of my life …

… and, sadly, I barely noticed her go.

Eclipsed by two warring factions, each cursed with an overriding obsession, she executed her departure with a gracious dignity. And, strange as it might seem, I never truly realised that she'd gone until the deafening silence of the kitchen became overwhelming …

… that animated, confrontational chatter …

… absent …

… that chair across the table …

… empty …

… that scent … her scent …

… gone …

… and that defiance … that barefaced defiance …

… God, how I missed her.

It was as if I'd suddenly woken from a dream – a long, disturbing, exhausting dream.

My lovely firebrand had turned to shadow and, tragically, I'd never seen it happen.

24

With her love rival gone, Duchess embraced the rigours of the somersault with renewed gusto – a startling metamorphosis that breathed new purpose into my fickle couple. In fact, the improvement was nothing short of miraculous as both dolphins swamped me with a psychic renewal of their team vows.

This pledge, however, was delivered with a sobering message: our dream team could only ever consist of three – never four. Interlopers such as Carol would not be tolerated. My jealous Atlanteans had given me an unmistakeable slap across the wrists – a sharp reminder that it was time to move on.

We were at our peak, heading the first division, and had to stay on top of our game. Especially now, because next stop …

… movie land.

❦ 25 ❧

The big day!

Duchess and Herb'e's trick list made gratifying reading: three double opening bows, handshake, double tail slap, retrieval of rings, retrieval of hat and sunglasses, three double hurdles, three double hoops, toothbrush, double back tail walk, singing, boat tow, tail football, yes thank you/no thank you, double two and a half back somersault, solo highball, lifebelt, double fish hand, solo fish mouth, double body spins, double two and a half forward somersault and wave – all topped off by three spectacular closing bows.

Fabulous! Without doubt, the finest show routine of the aqua-circus and truly worthy of cinematic documentation. The only trick missing from this impressive line-up was the beaching – a new goal I was determined to pursue once filming was over.

But for now, it was all about today – all about delivering "The Greatest Show on Earth"!

❧ 26 ❧

Dan and I watched, transfixed, as an invading army descended on the pool – a chaotic call to arms of techno-geeks, accompanied by a clashing concerto of tripods, cameras and microphones. It was impossible not to be impressed as they positioned their equipment with meticulous precision. We marvelled as they checked and double-checked their weapons of choice – a co-ordinated pincer movement overseen by a silent and uncharacteristically edgy Backhouse.

"Something about this set-up doesn't seem right," Dan whispered, as we watched from the stage. "Doesn't it strike you as weird that there won't be an audience present for filming? I mean, Head Office usually makes such a song and dance about publicity opportunities like this, yet none of the Company bigwigs are even here."

Dan had a point. "Yeah, come to think of it, it is a bit unusual."

A short pause as my astute partner continued his ruminations. "Who commissioned the filming, anyway? Do you know?"

"No, Backhouse never said, but I would imagine it's one of the big American marine parks. You know what the Yanks are like – if they see something they want, they don't let the grass grow under their feet, do they?"

Dan chewed on his mouth thoughtfully. "It's just occurred to me … Do you think Head Office even knows about this?"

"Knows about what?"

"This show – the filming?"

I felt as if I'd been sitting in a dark room and someone had just turned on the light. "You know, Dan, you could be right. It wouldn't surprise me one bit if they didn't, because Backhouse is looking decidedly furtive, even by his standards. In fact, this whole thing is beginning to stink!"

We continued to watch …

… Backhouse continued to stand guard …

… the camera crew continued to work in total silence.

The situation was so abnormal as to feel positively intimidating. It was quite literally them and us: two opposing armies separated by a body of water.

"Just what's with all this cloak and dagger stuff, anyway?" Dan muttered, sneaking another glance across the pool. "There's no need for it. It's not natural. I mean, what the hell's he up to?"

"Not a clue. But, knowing Backhouse, I wouldn't mind betting that it's something dodgy. He's got a lot of sway in animal circles, so he'll have his sticky fingers in a helluva lot of pies."

"Animal circles?" Dan growled. "He couldn't give a damn about animals. All he cares about is what's in it for him."

"Well, Dan, you know what they say: 'Animal conservation and animal exploitation are two sides of the same coin.'"

By the time we'd finished grumbling, the crew were almost ready to start filming, having erected three large cameras around the pool: the first covering the left side, the second covering the right, and the third focussed on the centre.

"Well, no use fretting about it now, Dan – we've got work to do. By my reckoning, we have an hour at most before they're ready to start shooting. So let's go make ourselves beautiful …

… and get this show on the road."

⟨ 27 ⟩

Ready at last.

With the fish prepared and stage sparkling, all I needed now was a final word with my two stars. Duchess and Herb'e, clearly looking forward to another team talk, excitedly rested their chins on the poolside.

"Right, you two, this is it – your big chance to show the world just how clever you are. So make the most of it."

An animated squawk alerted me to possible mischief-making.

"That especially goes for you, Herb'e. I need you to be a good boy, okay?"

Herb'e flashed a toothy grin before wriggling his head further onto the stage.

"Aww, you worry too much, David ..."

He gave me that look – the one that spelt trouble.

"I mean it, Herb'e, I don't want any problems! This is your *show, so don't let yourself down."*

A wagging tongue pull did nothing to allay my fears.

What an imp of mischief! But, imp or not, he was right – I shouldn't let myself get uptight, because my ever-dependable Duchess would always be there to keep him in check.

"Okay, people, let's give them a show to remember!"

❧ 28 ❧

The performance opens with the customary introductory slurry, then I'm on.

Blimey, this is weird! I'm supposed to be a seasoned performer, yet stepping onto a stage without the applause of a real, live audience feels bizarre. Reminds me of that nightmarish Welby première when just no one bothered to put their hands together.

And looking into the gloom of a deserted auditorium isn't helping, either.

In fact, this whole thing feels decidedly unreal. Even the filter room seems to be emitting an eerie wail – a haunting lament for an excluded Joe Public.

And, as if things aren't bad enough, there's Backhouse – that lone figure slinging hate-daggers from the shadows of the auditorium. I can feel their barbs from here. How he must loathe me!

"David, what's wrong with you? The show's started. Concentrate!"

There's no fooling Duchess – she's already detected the shriek of alarm bells.

"Ignore him, David, or you'll ruin the show!"

She senses my inner turmoil and sees how my state of mind is affecting the performance. Somehow, I've got to turn down the psychic radio, otherwise I'll blow its fuse – and, in all probability, the show itself.

But I'm sharp, so sharp that my inbuilt receiver is trawling the airwaves, picking up anything and everything. Not just words, but thoughts … emotions …

… *his* emotions.

It's unnerving … I can feel him, actually *feel* him …

… Backhouse is projecting a hate storm my way – a hate storm powerful enough to invoke a fury. His insidious loathing is battering back the door to my dark side, threatening to release what lurks within …

… that caged animal …

… the tethered beast …

… the monster from the id.

I dare not give way … I must contain the demon within, or something terrible might ensue …

… ensue …

… ensue …

…

…

A flash behind my eyes, and my vantage point has changed …

… I'm no longer on the stage, but floating in the auditorium, watching the other *me* going through the motions …

… a puppetmaster pulling on invisible strings.

I hang outside time … less than six feet away from *him* …

… six short feet away from all that pent-up hate.

…

Hate …

Hate …

…

… YOU WANT HATE … I'LL GIVE YOU HATE …!

…

…

So this is how it feels …

…

… fingers snatching at his scrawny neck …

…

… thumbs squeezing on his jugulars …

…

… spirit hands choking the passage of his life's blood …

…

So this is how it feels …

…

…

…

"David! No! No!"

…

What … what are you doing, Capello …?

Let go, you idiot! For God's sake, release him! Get back to the stage fast, or you'll lose everything you've ever worked for!

But I can't release him … can't let go …

…

So this is how it feels …

…

"David! David! Please!"

…

Duchess … my beautiful, beautiful Duchess …

…

"Come back … come back … come back to me!"

Got to listen to Duchess … got to escape this rage … cast this murderous vision from my mind …

But how? How do I find my way home?

…

…

The mirror …!

I need the mirror … need its magic … need to let it wash over me, cleanse me, purify me …

Must think of the mirror, only the mirror …

She's calling from the mirror …

Duchess … my beautiful, beautiful Duchess …

Got to move forward … can't allow myself to be stuck in this poisonous pit of an auditorium any longer …

It's all about the mirror – nothing else – only the mirror …

Look deep into its waves and find her … She calls from where the water's swell melts into one glistening plane …

Feel her drawing you back … back …

… back to her side …

… *her* side …

…

...

Time hits light speed, crashing headlong into the shriek of my whistle ...
It's over.

The show's over.

The filming's over.

My psychic attack is over ...

... and the shadow ballet is captured forever within a timeless bubble of film.

Amazingly, the performance has gone well. Duchess and Herb'e have delivered the full somersault routine in perfect unison − a job well done, despite my astral desertion.

But with the stress of the show behind me, I find my attention drawn back, back into the pit.

There he is. Backhouse − a silent figure, struggling to maintain an air of detachment.

I meticulously scan his countenance, and our eyes can't help but meet.

Odd, very odd ...

Normally, he looks straight through me. But this time, it's different. His cocky façade is compromised, and I'm conscious of his unease.

Does he know?

Did he sense my psychic attack?

Did he actually feel the pressure of my hands on his throat?

Or is my imagination just running wild?

Maybe I'm losing it ...

... maybe the Backhouse grind has finally sent me over the edge.

Can't be sure ... Must look harder ...

No ... distress is etched across his features; confusion in his eyes; and that superior expression is gone.

He knows ... he knows ...

... not my imagination ...

... he knows all right.

I have a victory, and, as I wallow in my triumph, I find it difficult not to smirk − a payback that sends him slinking to his office.

The slamming of a door, and he's gone.

And so have the film crew.

They certainly didn't hang around ... couldn't get away quick enough.

And who can blame them? The atmosphere in the dolphinarium is deteriorating faster than the water.

This can't go on much longer. It can't …

Something's got to give.

❦ 29 ❧

Thinking, thinking, thinking … Did it really happen?

Did my psychic attack of yesterday actually take place, or is my mental state so utterly compromised that I am no longer able to distinguish between fantasy and reality?

I still vehemently believe in my theory of the dolphin mansion of countless rooms: linked hideaways that operate simultaneously yet independently of one another – an incredible feat in multitasking that I have previously never been able to master. Yet, only twenty-four hours ago, there I was, quite literally in two places at the same time.

So, again, I have to ask myself, did I actually initiate a psychic attack on Backhouse?

Yes … yes, I did.

I'd always believed that my affinity with my Atlanteans would greatly advance my mental powers, but recent events have now convinced me that I have indeed been elevated to a higher level. The evolution of my psyche is all too real.

I've seemingly developed the capacity to space hop – first evident when I joined with Herb'e in his sensational forward somersault.

This new phenomenon can only be down to my spiritual moulding of my *Perfect Pair* – an obsessive work in progress that persistently pushes back the boundaries. But it's also becoming ever more apparent that I am not the only one in pursuit of an obsession.

My beautiful Duchess has always delighted in reminding me that the *connection* works both ways, creating a forum where diverse peoples may interact – an impartial place where intelligent beings can quite literally talk the talk. A premise that throws up yet another mind-boggling question: just who here at Hendle is being viewed as a work in progress?

My dream team – or me?

❦ 30 ❧

A fraught two weeks later, the filtration engineers began work on Hendle's decrepit water system – and there was little doubt that they'd arrived just in the nick of time. Despite the increased number of backwashes, the pool water had turned to a deep olivine green, and all four dolphins were again showing signs of skin blistering.

Although I welcomed the engineers' arrival, my enthusiasm was tempered by an unanticipated downside: during the stripping and replacement of the existing filter beds, the entire water system would have to be shut down for up to ten days. This was crippling news, as it would mean no water flow at all – a catastrophe that would leave the pool stagnant.

This meant I'd now be forced to administer chlorine by the bucket – an extremely dangerous practice, which might lead to my dolphins swimming through clouds of stinging chemicals. Yet without this, the pool itself would quickly turn toxic.

This situation was extremely serious and, whether I liked it or not, Backhouse had to be alerted. So, for me, it was again time to enter the lion's den.

"No problem," he replied tersely. "The engineers have assured me that once the new filter beds are operational, we'll see a remarkable improvement in water quality."

As always, his attitude was as predictable as it was confrontational.

"That might be true for *good* water," I argued, "but we haven't got good water. Our water is already bad, and getting worse with every passing day. Add another two weeks with no filtration whatsoever and all we'll have left is a poisonous swamp."

Backhouse sucked in his cheeks agitatedly before delivering his final dismissive remark. "As always, Mr Capello, it seems that you would rather embrace the dramatic, whereas I would prefer to listen to the experts – something you should try doing for once."

His sheer contempt for me was again twisting his logic, distorting his interpretation of just what the engineers had actually said. And, as always, he was in no mood to risk loss of face by seeking clarification.

"Okay, Tommy. For argument's sake, let's say you're right. Let's say the new filters are gonna do the trick. Just one question: what do you think is going to happen when they're eventually switched on? I mean, come on, don't you remember what happened at Welby?"

Reminding Backhouse of yet another one of his glorious cockups was like waving a red rag to a bull.

"The Welby situation was completely different," he snarled, "and I don't intend to discuss this matter any further. Understand?"

I understood all right – understood that all our little chat had achieved was to wind us both up even further. Reaffirmation – if ever I needed it – that holding even the simplest of conversations with Backhouse was now impossible.

It was soul-destroying. In just over one month since his return from Welby, Backhouse's unyielding grind had totally erased the euphoria of the shadow ballet. Our relationship had deteriorated to such an extent that even his presence shredded my nerves – something he realised only too well.

He recognised that I was becoming ever more brittle. All he had to do was keep up the pressure until I snapped. Only then, when he deemed me at my most vulnerable, would he snake in for the kill and steal his prize …

… my legacy … my obsession …

… *my* Duchess and Herb'e.

❧ 31 ❧

A voice bellowed hoarsely from the filter room. "Right, lads, we're almost ready to start 'em up. Just ten more minutes …"

This was it: D-day – the big switch on. Only ten minutes more before the new filters became operational.

As the seconds ticked by, Backhouse and I waited on opposite sides of the pool, both desperately trying to avoid eye contact and thankful for the expanse of water lying between us.

Water … the term barely applied following the torturous longer-than-expected fifteen-day shutdown. The Hendle pool now bore all the trappings of a tropical swamp rather than a dolphin arena. A foul stench permeated the air, and my enchanted mirror sported a green-hued overcoat, through which rigid grey dorsal fins sluggishly and intermittently sliced.

"Not long now, lads," the voice boomed. "Right, that's it! Here we go!"

No sooner had he given the word than I felt a deep rumble erupt from the belly of the pool. Seconds later, powerful air bubbles munched their way through the gloom, prising the green coat apart. I held my breath as the moss broth bubbled and spat, reminiscent of a witch's cauldron. No one moved – not a muscle twitched – as all eyes remained glued to this titanic collision of air and water: the re-enactment of a primordial battle.

Then it happened …

The surface of the pool suddenly lurched upwards, vomiting a cloud of oily, black sand. We stared wide-eyed with shock as the tormented arena bellyached and groaned before belching out discs of what appeared to be congealed tar.

"Oh, my God, what the hell's that?" Dan screamed. "It looks like paint ..."

I looked on in horror as Dan's terrible observation slammed home. "God, it *is* paint – it's the filter coating!" Swinging around to face a noticeably shaken Backhouse, I yelled, "Quick, we've got to get that stuff out of the water! If it gets into the dolphins' blowholes, it'll kill 'em!"

Chaos erupted as everyone – Backhouse included – dashed frantically around the pool, snatching at literally anything capable of holding water: buckets, sump grills, scoops and even dive masks. It was bedlam!

"Where's it come from?" Dan shouted. "How on earth has paint got into the water?"

I didn't reply – couldn't reply – time was a luxury we couldn't afford. All that mattered now was removing the black, sticky gloop spotting the mirror's face.

On hearing our cries, a crowd of ashen-faced engineers streamed from the bowels of the filter room, buckets in hand.

"Come on, we've got to keep that paint away from the dolphins!"

The mêlée continued for a full hour before the panic finally subsided – a near catastrophe that left a horde of gasping figures littered around the pool's walkways.

Despite none of my charges being harmed, I was furious, absolutely furious. Teeth clenched, I glared at the head engineer.

"I'm sorry, so sorry ... I just never thought about the dolphins," he pleaded. "If anything had happened to them, I would never have forgiven myself. You see, we normally carry out this type of work on an empty pool, so any excess paint coming away from the filters isn't a problem. I don't know what to say ..."

He was not only apologetic, but also clearly distressed, so there seemed little point in upsetting him further. Nevertheless, I was all too aware of just how this might have ended.

"Okay, okay ... no harm done ... we've been lucky," I assured him soberly. "But we still have a problem ..."

The white-faced engineer looked at me beseechingly. "Problem ... what problem?"

My gaze led him to the dense sand clouds churning around the pool. "What do we do with that lot?"

"Well, under normal circumstances, it would eventually work its way through the system. But this water's so filthy, I just assumed you'd be dumping?"

On hearing this, Backhouse visibly stiffened. The comment had obviously hit a raw nerve — one that immediately sent him scurrying back to his office …

… a stark indication of trouble to come.

Once the engineers had gone, I knew that I'd again find myself in the unenviable position of having to trudge to Backhouse's inner sanctum to plead for permission to dump the pool …

… permission he was bound to refuse.

For me, this latest visit could only end one way: more frustration, more humiliation …

… courtesy of the Backhouse grind.

≼ 32 ≽

"We don't need a dump now that the new system is operational. Just give it a few days and the water will clear itself," Backhouse argued. "Besides, we can't afford to lose any more shows."

Even after hearing what the engineer had said, all Backhouse cared about was money – or, should I say, the loss of it.

"I don't give a toss how good these filters are, they can't work miracles," I countered. "This water's dead – stone dead – and it stinks to high heaven. We have to ditch. We have no choice."

Backhouse fell silent, his air of confidence momentarily dissipated. Sensing his doubt, I foolishly pushed my luck. "Tommy, I warned you about this. Except for the paint, it's virtually a repeat of what happened at Welby."

Me and my big mouth! I'd again waved the red rag. The last thing he needed was another reminder of his gross incompetence.

"I will not allow a pool dump under any circumstances," he shrieked, renewed. "We don't need one. What we *need* is to pen the dolphins and shock the pool. One huge chlorine hit and all the toxins will be burned out."

Not for the first time, I'd destroyed my advantage. So, disheartened by my own stupidity and desperate to avoid further confrontation, I reluctantly caved in to his directive …

… a shameful placation that would subject everything I held dear to yet even more suffering.

clyde rules

❧ 33 ❧

Like a scolded child, I sealed my four charges into stagnant prisons, painfully aware that they were now paying the price for my feeble capitulation. For eighteen hours, I watched them drift in cramped cesspools whilst Backhouse implemented his ill-planned water bleaching policy – an exercise that, as expected, ended in abject failure.

Yet again, I'd stood idly by and allowed my charges to suffer.

But no longer – my shameful pacification of Backhouse was at an end.

"Tommy, if *you* don't give me the permission I need to dump this pool, then I'll seek it elsewhere. I'll contact Head Office personally and make this official. I mean, it Tommy – I'll do it! I've done it before. Remember what happened with Forrester."

As expected, my ultimatum provoked a hostile reaction.

"How dare you threaten *me*! I'm your general manager … You don't tell *me* what to do … I tell *you*."

Not this time, sunshine – the gloves were off, and I was in no mood for backing down.

"Either you make that call, Tommy … or I will!"

❧ 34 ❧

Backhouse was visibly seething. The last thing he wanted was Rogers hearing about his relentless scheming.

"I'm not bluffing, Tommy. If you don't pick up that 'phone, I'm gonna tell him just what's been going on here … So make that call!"

Desperate to maintain the rose-tinted façade that he'd peddled to Head Office, Backhouse begrudgingly yielded to my demand – a capitulation that left him rabid, confirmed by the vigour with which he slammed down the telephone receiver.

"Okay, Capello, you've got what you want. Satisfied?"

Backhouse might be down, but he certainly wasn't out. His lips quivered into a supercilious smirk.

"As you're here anyway, I have something to say. It's about Dan. In my opinion, he isn't up to the job, so I'm informing you here and now that I intend to replace him at the earliest opportunity. Is that understood?"

Payback time Backhouse style – and a spitefully uninformed observation for a man who'd spent most of his time skulking at Welby. My general manager was again striking where he thought he could hurt me most – a tactic he'd used successfully in the past. Couldn't get rid of the Company's only trainer, but *could* get rid of his mate.

"Oh, so Dan's not up to the job, is he?" I sneered. "Well, there's a surprise! Repeating the Vance scenario, are we? Well, go for it, Tommy, because this time you won't get away with it so easy …

… I'm not gonna let you or your rotten spite tear my world apart again."

❧ 35 ❧

Backhouse left me to stew for another two days, repeatedly postponing the promised ditch in the vain hope that the pool would miraculously clear itself.

In the meantime, a distraught Dan pulled me aside to tell me he already knew that Backhouse intended to sack him.

"I've been expecting something like this for a while. There can only be one boss, Dave, and – unfortunately for us – he's it. The way you keep challenging him makes you dangerous, so he'll take you out any way he can. You've got to remember, when it comes to scruples, Backhouse doesn't have any."

As always, Dan's observations were spot on. Backhouse habitually operated in the safety of the shadows, from where he could do the most damage – a strategy I'd have to adopt if I were to stand any chance of countering him. So, dump or no dump, I still intended to make that long overdue call to Rogers.

"Dan, I'm gonna tell Rogers just what a dirty, rotten, underhanded rat Backhouse really is. Tell him how *his* golden boy has been making everyone's life a misery."

Dan was quick to caution. "Now just hold your horses, Dave, and consider what you're about to do. You already know that the men in suits will stick together. They'll view an attack on Backhouse as an attack on them. In other words, you've got no chance! *You'll* end up gone and Backhouse will have what he wants – total control over everyone and everything, including Duchess and Herb'e."

More words of wisdom. Any trouble between Backhouse and me could only result in my getting the short end of the stick. Rogers would have no choice but to back his general manager, which might well see me out of a job – a supremely gratifying outcome for Backhouse, as, with me out of the way, he would be free to claim his prize and wipe clean any trace of my existence.

It would be easy. First, sack all my colleagues. Second, eradicate any links tying me to Duchess and Herb'e. This would allow him to seize my legacy with impunity, as with me gone and no one left to set the record straight, I'd quickly become a ghost …

… no, not even a ghost …

… worse …

… a nothing.

I had to hand it to him, my general manager had certainly done his groundwork. His unyielding grind had taken a severe toll, leaving me fragile and vulnerable. He knew it was just a matter of time before I'd react by doing something stupid – something unforgiveable.

Then, he'd strike.

Backhouse was so close to his dream; so close to the victory he craved; so close, he could almost touch it …

… the kingdom, the power and the glory …

… Tommy Backhouse …

… the new face behind *The Perfect Pair*.

❮ 36 ❯

"I don't care anymore, Dan," I wailed. "I can't continue living like this. I just can't. I've got to fight back. If I'm on my way out, I'm going with a bang, not a whimper."

I was desperate – my entire being literally screaming – yet I knew I had to try to stay calm. I couldn't go charging in like a bull in a china shop. I had to be precise. So, soothed by Dan's steadying influence, I decided to take a step back and finalise my decision. It took some heartfelt deliberation, but my decision remained unchanged. I knew exactly what I had to do – and when I did it, there would be no turning back.

Hands shaking nervously, I picked up the telephone receiver to dial Rogers' number, fully aware that once that ringtone ceased, I'd be in the lap of the gods.

"Good afternoon, this is Mr Rogers' office. Can I help you?"

Relief washed over me. Thank God – it wasn't Rogers, but his personal secretary, Pam. Even so, I struggled to find my words.

"Hello, can I help you?"

It was now or never.

"Hello, Pam, it's David Capello from Hendle. I urgently need to speak to Mr Rogers."

She clearly sensed my discomfort, because a note of concern softened her tone. "I'm sorry, David, but Mr Rogers isn't here at the moment. Is there anything I can do to help?"

Rogers out – my luck was holding. I'd met Pam on numerous occasions in the past, and we'd always got on well. So well, in fact, that she'd managed to procure tickets for my sister to see the Osmond gig when they'd first played City Hall.

Responding to her gentle encouragement, I began to recount the plethora of underhand tricks that Backhouse had subjected me to over the last year – poignant recollections that left me on the verge of tears.

"I can't stand it anymore, Pam. Backhouse is destroying everything I've worked for, and I just don't know what to do."

So much for my stiff upper lip – it had totally collapsed.

"Please, David, try not to upset yourself," she soothed. "As soon as Mr Rogers gets in, I'll make him fully aware of the situation. In the meantime, try not to do anything rash – Mr Backhouse isn't worth it!"

Warming words of comfort from a lady who clearly had little time for my general manager.

"Remember, David," she pressed, "you have been a major player in the success of Mr Rogers' dolphin project, so don't allow Mr Backhouse to force you out. And don't worry about Mr Rogers, either – leave *him* to me."

Pam's genuine concern and promise of support gave me new hope. Pam had been Rogers' personal secretary for many years, so if anyone could plead my case, it was she. Incredible as it seemed, in my darkest hour, I'd found a new ally – one supremely skilled in the art of boardroom strategy.

This extraordinary lady was the charm offensive I needed to at least guarantee me a hearing.

❦ 37 ❧

"All right, Dan, Backhouse has finally given the go-ahead, so let's get them sealed into the holding pens fast! This water's dire, so the quicker we start the dump, the better."

My use of the word "dire" was no exaggeration. The thick green soup was growing darker by the hour – a deterioration that would accelerate rapidly within the stagnant pens. For my poor dolphins, their upcoming thirty-hour confinement in these filth-ridden boxes would seem like a lifetime. An ordeal that could – and should – have been avoided, had I not allowed Backhouse to have his way.

Still, it was too late to worry about that now. It was over and done, and no amount of recrimination could turn back the clock.

As for the man himself, Backhouse had not ventured from his office for the best part of the day – although, to be honest, that wasn't such a bad thing, as neither one of us could bear to even look at the other.

The overriding requirement now was that the pool ditch should go well, meaning I needed to keep a clear head – not easy considering the way my thoughts kept wandering back to the kitchen telephone.

Surely, Pam had passed my message to Rogers by now; told him how dangerously close to the edge I was?

Surely, she'd stressed the gravity of my situation.

Surely, she'd …

… God, this was torture!

Why hadn't Rogers returned my call?

Why?

❦ 38 ❧

With the backwash in full swing, it won't be long before my volunteers arrive – a ragtag army of people from every walk of life, all eager to be involved in the ultimate dolphin experience.

God, they must be mad – absolutely bonkers – but what would I do without them?

Nice to see young Graham walking through the door, 'cause he's definitely my favourite. Mind you, of late, he *has* been noticeable by his absence. Can't say I blame him – the atmosphere in this place has been horrible.

Oh, wait a minute, who's that? *She's* a bit of all right … haven't seen *her* before! Wonder who she's with? I mean, she must have come with someone, because the dolphinarium isn't the easiest place to get to … Ah! Would you believe it? So that's why Graham's been missing – the lucky little sod's got himself a girlfriend … and a pretty one too!

Funny seeing Graham with a girl; brings home just how quickly life can change.

Boy, mine certainly did …

Was it really only three years ago when all this started?

I can still remember standing on that grimy platform at City Railway Station, dreaming of fame and fortune, clear blue waters, golden sands and palm trees stretching as far as the eye could see – not a single dolphin in sight!

Was that *really* only three years ago? Seems like a lifetime!

I can still see my first newspaper headline: *David lands a dream of a job …*

… the glamour …

… the glitz …

... the celebrity ...

...

... the constant wet ...

... the aching bones ...

... the stink of stale fish ...

...

... the injustice ...

... the rotten, terrible injustice ...

...

God, talk about naïve!

Still, back then I was just a kid who didn't know any better. A kid? Blimey, just listen to me – I sound like an old man! Even worse, I feel like one too, and I'm only twenty-one.

"Hey, can anyone spare a fag? I'm gasping for a smoke!"

I really need to bum a nicotine fix ... take my mind off things ...

... the dire conditions that my dolphins are having to put up with in those rotten, filth-ridden pens ...

... not to mention that bloody 'phone call from Rogers ... the one I've been waiting for ... the one that *still* hasn't come.

What a life! Forty-eight hours stuck in this bloody hellhole without a smoke. Could it get any worse?

"Dave, there's someone at the back door to see you!"

God, for a minute there I thought that someone was actually gonna offer me a cigarette!

"See *me*? What ... at this time of night?"

Who in their right mind would be wandering around a deserted safari park at this time of night?

Night? Did I actually say night? Morning would be a better word! Well, duty calls, as they say, so I'd better go check out just who -

"My God, I don't believe it! What the heck are *you* doing here?"

❧ 39 ❧

"Now there's a sight for sore eyes! Will Chadderton – I thought you had a dolphinarium of your own to look after?"

My ex-manager's presence lights up the room. Thankfully, some things never change. I've certainly missed him since his move to Welby.

"Sit yourself down, Will. Kettle's on, so I'll make you a cuppa tea. And please, *please* tell me that you're here to stay!"

My eyes widen enviously as he pulls a pack of cigarettes from his pocket …

… cigarettes …

"No such luck, David. I'm just passing through. I've been stuck in a meeting all day at Head Office. While I was there, Pam told me that you were dumping the pool tonight."

A meeting at Head Office – a meeting that *had* to be chaired by Rogers.

"Anyway, as I'm in the area, I thought I'd drop by and give you some grief."

Did he say grief? No thank you – I've had enough grief to last me a lifetime.

"By the way, lovely brew, David – just what the doctor ordered."

Fumbling for his lighter, he fiddles annoyingly with a cigarette …

… a cigarette … *his* cigarette.

Will hasn't mentioned Backhouse yet. Wonder why? Does he know? After all, he has spoken to Pam. Surely she must have told him?

My nostrils twitch as his nicotine fix scents the air …

… I could murder that cigarette.

"By the way, where's that general manager of yours hiding?"

73

Ahhh … finally …

"It would be unforgiveable of me not to pop in and say hello."

Say hello? It's not like Will to play games. Maybe Pam hasn't told him, after all? In fact, maybe she hasn't told Rogers, either? In which case, what do I do? Do I tell Will about the nightmare I'm having with Backhouse, or do I just keep shtum?

Good God, I could murder that fag!

Pointing the way to Backhouse's office, I muster a pleading smile. "Er … before you go, Will, I don't suppose you've got a spare cig I could cadge? Only – with the ditch and all – I've had no time to get to the shops and I'm gasping … Desperate, in fact …"

"Blimey, David, some things never change!"

What does he mean by that?

Beaming a large grin, he slings me his pack of cigarettes. "Here – have 'em! There's about eight left, so those should keep you going for a while."

Hallelujah! A result! It's about time something went right for a change.

Thinking about it, things haven't turned out too badly after all. I'm now eight fags to the good and Will's impromptu visit should keep Backhouse entertained long enough for me to organise my volunteers. Good old Will!

"Now … has anyone got a light?"

❧ 40 ❧

It's the early hours of the morning and the pool is finally empty, which means I can at last galvanise my volunteers into action. Over the last two and a half years, the basin has become coated with a stubborn green algae, which has proved near impossible to remove. So now is the perfect time to get rid of it, as we can use the chemical agents otherwise banned when the pool is full. A chance like this won't come again, so we have to take advantage. However, we have only a limited window in time, because we still have four dolphins drifting in near-toxic pens, and the sooner we get them out, the better.

I hear the echo of a slamming door and the sound of heavy footsteps.

Two people.

Then I hear that irritating, condescending voice – *his* voice – thundering from the auditorium.

"Come on, you lot, put your backs into it! This isn't a holiday camp. I want this place spick and span and up and running for tomorrow afternoon! We've lost enough show time as it is."

The cheek of *him*!

Backhouse … crawled out of his hole … barking orders … trying to justify his position by putting everyone else down.

From the base of the pool, I can't see *him*, but I can certainly hear *him*. Even worse, I can feel *him* – his malevolence sets my teeth on edge. Glancing around, I notice that everyone is keeping their heads down. Not one single, solitary soul looks up …

… except me.

75

I clock *him* as he peers into the basin, strutting around like a peacock, posturing arrogantly.

Our eyes can't help but meet, and I instinctively know, know that he's told Will – told him how much he despises me.

I maintain my fixed stare as my lord and master swaggers around the pool's perimeter before imperiously swinging onto the ladders to begin his downward descent.

That's my cue to depart – get out. There isn't enough room down here to accommodate the two of us.

A sheepish Will puts out his hand to greet me as I step from the topmost rung of the ladder and onto the stage. He hardly dares to make eye contact – can't even look me in the face.

Yeah, Will knows all right – his whole demeanour is telegraphing his discomfort.

He musters a half-hearted laugh. "You've certainly got a big job on here, David. I wouldn't fancy having to …"

Will's trying to lighten the mood, smooth things over with small talk.

But it isn't working.

I'm just not hearing, 'cause all I can hear is *him*: Backhouse and his snide remarks – remarks directed at everyone else, but meant for me.

God, how I loathe him!

My inbuilt radio is thundering, blasting so loudly that my ears are actually throbbing …

… can't hear anything, only *his* abuse …

… can't stand it anymore … can't stand it …

… losing control.

Abruptly, Will's voice is gone.

The radio, *my* radio …

… silent.

I'm in a vortex, uncertain of my bearings …

… then comes that explosive blast of sound …

… that re-connection.

"You've got what you want, Capello, so don't push your luck!"

It's *him* – Backhouse – his twisted mind convinced that I'm bad-mouthing him to Will, sniping behind his back …

… something else the mealy-mouthed bastard's managed to get wrong.

Will's eyes widen, and he shies away, turning his face aside in an attempt to pretend that he hasn't heard what Backhouse has just said.

But he doesn't fool me. Will heard all right …

… and so did everyone else …

… and, what's more, Backhouse isn't finished. In fact, he's just getting started.

"You'd be wise to remember just who's boss around here, Capello! Just which one of us is actually calling the shots. Something the rest of you would do well to remember too …"

He's trying to humiliate me in front of my friends! How dare he! How dare he!

The periphery of my vision distorts and tunnels downwards, downwards toward the pool floor to fix on the loathsome figure of my illustrious general manager – a man I have come to despise.

His lips are moving, but I cannot hear him. There's only a distant thunder…

Will ceases to exist …

My volunteers cease to exist …

Only Backhouse remains – a solitary figure spitting venom.

I'm looking down the barrel of a gun …

… I bare my teeth … ready to pull the trigger.

Lousy bastard! You rotten, lousy, arrogant bastard! Playing the big shot … trying to put me down in front of everybody …

… well, I'm not 'avin' it!

Snarling, I swing around to grab the heavy fire hose suspended on the wall, frantically tearing it from its reel.

How dare you! How dare you!

One gargantuan tug sees its huge bulk coiled around my body. Muscles knot and strain as I drag its reptilian carcase across the stage.

"Don't push your luck!" he said. Well, there's only one man around here pushing his luck …

… and that's *HIM*!

Whirling the regulator to full capacity, I wrestle with the reptile's body as it swells into life; fight to control its writhing python head; battle the venomous blood surge that races through its innards …

… velocity building …

… pressure building …

… detonation …

… a hammer-force explosion smashing Backhouse full in the chest.

Payback time, you rotten, lousy sod!

The sheer power of the jet blasts him off his feet, brutally slamming him onto his backside.

Shouting … people shouting … people screaming … but my frenzied roar drowns them out.

"How dare you! How dare you!"

Gorging myself on his utter humiliation, I send him unceremoniously slithering across the pool's concrete base.

"Not such a big shot now, are yer!"

Volunteers scatter, dashing frantically towards ladders in an attempt to escape the fallout of my insanity.

They needn't worry – I have only one target in sight …

… *HIM*!

Scrabbling on hands and knees, he struggles to follow them.

No chance, sunshine – tonight you're mine and you're not going anywhere!

You rat! You rotten, lousy, devious rat!

I continue to grapple with the writhing serpent in my grasp, then – suddenly – I'm conscious of the tears rolling down my cheeks …

… crying …

… I'm actually, physically crying …

… a release of all that bottled-up heartache and frustration.

As the tears flow, my anger subsides, drawing me back to a blurry reality.

I feel sick, ready to vomit.

What's happened? What have I done?

I feel a gentle pressure on my arm.

"David, please stop … You've got to stop. You can't do this."

Will … it's Will … trying to calm me, soothe me, guide me home.

His touch draws me from the brink. I can't speak; just wipe away the tears with the back of my hand.

I feel strangely comatose as I watch Backhouse feverishly clambering up the ladder …

… battered, bruised and soaked, his degradation is complete.
But now comes the fallout – *my* time to pay the ferryman.
Humiliated, angry, vengeful …
… Backhouse is coming my way.

❦ 41 ❧

Only half with it … My head's in such a spin that everything around me appears alien. It's as though my mind has crashed – undergone a forced shutdown. I'm like a little boy lost, dazed and confused. Thank God for Will. Only he seems to realise the seriousness of my condition.

This is crazy! Come on, Capello! Come on! Pull yourself together!

I can hardly feel my arms and legs. Every last vestige of strength has melted away. Not only am I disorientated and weak, I'm frightened, terribly, terribly frightened. I'm in a nightmare without end.

God, he's in my face, his nose virtually touching mine – Backhouse, screaming uncontrollably. And I'm incapable of responding. I want to escape this madness. Find a dark place. Hide away …

But I can't escape …

What am I gonna do?

Will's wrestling to keep Backhouse off me, wedging himself between us. But that's not enough, not nearly enough. Backhouse is determined. He wants blood.

Can't rely on Will to save me. It's down to me – no one else but me. Somehow, I've got to pull myself together, find my way back …

But it's difficult. He's so close, he's smothering me. So near, he's stealing my breath. He's snarling, frenziedly battling to push Will aside. Backhouse wants to tear my head off, and I'm powerless to stop him.

What's wrong with me? Why can't I react?

His face pushes into mine – so close I feel his spittle stinging my cheeks.

Then, our eyes lock, and his hatred flicks the switch, delivering a surge of energy – a nuclear blast that cranks back my shoulders and straightens my spine.

Normal transmission has just been resumed …

… nothing wrong with me now.

I'm pumped up – a vampire feeding on my adversary's malice; gorging myself on his rage; devouring his nerve; sucking him dry.

He senses the change, snapping back his head to violently veer away.

"That's it, Capello, that's your lot! You're sacked! Do you hear me? Sacked! This time, you've overstepped the mark. You're washed-up! Finished!"

I hold my position.

"No one sacks me but the man who hired me – and that's Rogers!"

The full weight of Will's body is now pushing against me – just in case. Maybe he senses the change too.

"Are you listening, Backhouse? I don't take orders from *you* anymore. You're nothing but a rotten, lousy conman …"

Backhouse unleashes what he hopes will be his killer blow. "I've had enough of you, Capello. You've *just* committed a serious assault on a Company executive, and, as soon as the office opens, I'm calling Mr Rogers."

Time to strike back – lash out with words hard as steel. "I'll save you the trouble. You don't *need* to call Rogers – I already have!"

Rocked by this news, Backhouse turns ashen. He didn't expect that! No, my calling Rogers was the last thing he expected. Now everyone at Head Office will know that all the peace and harmony crap he's been feeding them is nothing but a sham – a barefaced lie. "Not so cocky now, are we, Backhouse?"

My adversary is wounded, floundering in the dark. Now he's the one who's lost and unsure. I've pulverized him with my revelation, left him struggling for words …

… struggling and tottering dangerously close to the pool's edge …

… the *empty* pool's edge.

Time suspends …

He's vulnerable …

…

… that's a thirteen-foot drop …

...

... a *thirteen-foot* drop ...

...

... a long way down ...

...

... a very, *very* long way down ...

...

If he were to slip over the top, the fall might easily kill him ...

...

A *thirteen-foot* drop ...!

I step forward.

"No! David! No! It's not worth it!" Will tightens his grip on my arms. "Just move away! Please – just move back!"

Will knows, knows just how far I'm prepared to go. And so does Backhouse – a shocking realisation that sends him scurrying clear of the abyss.

"Come on, David ..." I feel Dan's hand on my shoulder. "Let's get you back to the kitchen. You need to sit down."

I'm led off stage – zombie-like, everything a blur. I'm in a state of abject confusion – disorientation – with Backhouse's words ringing in my ears.

"You've just committed a serious assault on a Company executive. You're washed-up. FINISHED!"

He's right. I *am* washed-up. I *am* finished. There's no way I can ride out this storm. Not only have I lost my job, but I've also lost the two most important people in my life ...

... Duchess and Herb'e.

❦ 42 ❧

A hugely stressful twenty-four hours followed, leaving me with a numb, sickly feeling – the sort you get with a bereavement. And my ordeal wasn't over yet. Regardless of the hole I was in, I still had at least twelve hours of heavy graft to get through before I could safely release my dolphins from their watertight pens. For starters, this new water would need a full complement of salt, not to mention other treatments.

My charges' prisons were now so filthy that they resembled pits of stinking black sewage, meaning it was imperative to get them out quickly. Luckily, despite my clash with Backhouse, most of my volunteers had remained at their posts, which was more than could be said for the man himself, who had hightailed it out of the dolphinarium at super speed – hardly the kind of behaviour you'd expect from so-called senior management.

More troubling still, there was no sign of Will, either. Like Backhouse, it seemed that he too had wasted no time in beating a hasty retreat. And who could blame him? The poor bloke had only dropped in to say hello, and had ended up playing referee in a Hendle free-for-all. What a nightmare! Next time I saw him, I'd have a lot of apologising to do – if, indeed, there *was* a next time.

As I joined my volunteers in stacking the heavy salt bags around the pool walkways, I tried to pretend that this was just another day, although it was anything but.

My general manager and Will had disappeared, and the telephone call I'd banked on hadn't come – to say nothing of an agonisingly slow-filling pool and four distressed dolphins *still* trapped in atrocious conditions.

What a terrible, terrible mess!

Yet, as bad as this was, I knew it could only get worse – a lot worse ...

... I yet had to pay the price for my long-overdue rebellion.

❧ 43 ❧

Bleary-eyed, I watched as the last bags of salt emptied into the pool. Albeit cloudy, the water was finally fit for my dolphins to swim in. Just a pity about the contaminated water in the holding pens, which would flood back into the main arena on release of my charges. Hardly the best scenario, especially in light of the gruelling thirty hours plus we'd all endured to get it clean in the first place.

Still, it wasn't all doom and gloom: the re-conditioned filters should quickly dispose of any unwanted nasties and hopefully make the notorious Hendle water dumps a thing of the past.

"Right, boys and girls, it's time to get my babies out of their pens. They've been floating around in that muck long enough."

Within minutes, the dolphinarium was echoing to the grunts and groans of my helpers, as they wearily pulled on chains to raise the watertight doors.

"There you go, people, freedom at last!"

It was certainly good to see my Atlanteans racing exuberantly around the main pool, freeing up their cramped muscles and delivering a stunning display of aerial acrobatics – a truly fitting reward for the volunteers who had stayed behind to weather the storm.

"This is better than those rotten pens, isn't it? Bet you're glad to be free of them!"

The mirror's face reflected the generous smiles of my two favourite people and their West Coast companions.

"About time too! We thought you'd never let us out!"

Duchess and Herb'e's bubbly excitement reassured me that they'd suffered no ill effects from their long stay in the toxic pens.

"Well, since you've all been such good boys and girls, I'm declaring a show free day. So enjoy it while you can!"

Long live the rebellion!

With no Backhouse around to force the issue of shows, it was "happy holidays" and "sod the public"! For today, at least, there would be a rest day for man and dolphin alike. Nevertheless, despite the euphoria, I was sorely aware that this decision might well be my last, because, by now, Backhouse would have fully briefed Rogers.

"Don't worry, David, everything will work out. Have a little faith."

Duchess – a psychic message of hope, and, against all odds, one in which I couldn't help but believe.

"Have a little faith? God, Duch, you don't know what you're asking. Anyway, how did you know I was in so much trouble?"

Despite my mental fatigue, I received her reply loud and clear.

"Because, David, I am a part of you, as you are a part of me. Whatever happens to one happens to the other. You always forget, the connection works both ways."

❧ 44 ❧

Midday found Dan and me slumped across the kitchen table, wearily nursing mugs of hot tea.

As we reflected in bemused silence, I couldn't help but wonder ... When would it come? That damn telephone call ... the one telling me to pack my bags and go?

The waiting was torturous, almost as bad as waiting for Rogers' original call – the one that never came.

I afforded myself a cynical smile ...

... fat chance of that happening this time!

"Dave, I hate to say this," – thank God for Dan; the silence was becoming unbearable – "after last night's escapade, I can't possibly see you keeping your job. Backhouse will insist that Head Office sacks you."

I nodded forlornly. "Yeah, after what I did to his golden boy, I'm not holding out much hope. Rogers won't have any choice but to get rid of me." Sighing, I fumbled with Will's pack of cigarettes, hoping against hope that I hadn't already gobbled them all up.

One left – magic!

"You know, Dan, even now, I don't regret tackling Backhouse. I just wish that, instead of a dousing, I'd given him a good, hard thumping. Yeah! Now *that* would have been worth getting the sack for." I drew deeply on my nicotine comforter. "What's worrying me now is Duchess and Herb'e. Who's gonna take care of them when I'm gone? I mean, who? Backhouse couldn't give a toss. To him, they're just a means to an end."

Dan continued to sip his tea in thoughtful contemplation. "Who indeed?

Because I'm telling you, Dave, it won't be me. As soon as you get your cards, I'm gone. I have no intention of spending any more time than I have to in the company of that deplorable man."

I didn't reply – couldn't reply. Not for the first time, my dolphins would be picking up the tab for my insubordination – a price to which poor Baby and Scouse could already testify.

"Buuuut," – Dan's mood suddenly brightened – "maybe, just maybe, all is not lost. I mean, you still have an ace in the pack – you still have Duchess and Herb'e. After all, they're recognised as *The Perfect Pair*, the only show dolphins ever to perform the shadow ballet." He flashed me an impish smile. "Show dolphins that will work only for *you* – something Rogers and the Board know only too well. If the men in suits cut you now, there's every chance they'll lose their precious dream team. The question is, which way will they jump? Will they chance forfeiting Europe's top show simply to placate their general manager?"

Dan certainly had a point. My two babies were now worth a small fortune in the eyes of the dolphin world, and the prestige they brought to the Company was priceless. The Board members were now facing an unenviable dilemma: Tommy Backhouse was their general manager and the celebrity face of the dolphin project – an executive who had been assaulted by what some in the Company now classed as a presenter. Nevertheless, they were equally aware that this "presenter" held the crown jewels – Duchess and Herb'e. So, as Dan had pointed out, just which way would they jump?

Surely, they wouldn't – *couldn't* – turn on one of their own?

Or could they?

Whilst Dan was scrubbing the walkways, I busied myself mucking out the stinky hutch of our two resident penguins, Smelly and Worse – normally, the most reviled job in the dolphinarium; but today it took on a whole new meaning. After all, this could well be the last time I'd ever see the two little varmints, and – since they'd spent most of their unproductive lives making mine miserable – it seemed only fitting that I bid them one last farewell.

"Out you come, you two, that hutch needs a good bottoming and – Aargh! That smells bloody awful!" Even more toxic than usual due to their longer-than-expected incarceration for the pool dump. "Come on, I'm not telling you again – out!"

As always, when the prickly head of my trusty deck scrubber invaded their hallowed turf, the two would-be assassins prepared for battle.

"Aww, come on, you two, gimme a break! I've been on the go for three days and I'm absolutely knackered, so this is the last thing I need. Besides, I've only come to say goodbye." My words were like water off a duck's back – or, more appropriately, a penguin's back – as the two fiery-eyed Ninjas adopted combat mode.

"No you don't, you little sods – you're not 'avin' me today!"

Ringing … the distant ringing of a telephone – something that wouldn't hold much significance on any other day. But today wasn't just any other day: today was the day *after* the night before. I held my breath in anticipation, then Dan appeared at the kitchen door silently mouthing, "Head Office."

Head Office …

This was it – the call I'd been dreading. Nervously accepting the receiver,

I fully expected to hear Rogers giving me my marching orders. However, instead of the head honcho, I found myself speaking to someone I didn't even know.

"I presume I'm talking to David Capello, head trainer at Hendle?"

Head trainer? Well, there was a bonus – he could have asked for David Capello, *presenter*.

"We've been made aware that there has been an altercation between you and our general manager, Mr Backhouse, which I believe took place during the recent pool ditch. Obviously, the Board is extremely disappointed with your behaviour, Mr Capello. However, we have been informed that the problems between you and Mr Backhouse have been ongoing for some considerable time."

Who'd informed them? Surely not Backhouse? No, Pam ... it had to be Pam, Rogers' personal secretary.

"As you can well imagine, Mr Capello, your actions have placed the Board in a very difficult position."

He could say that again!

"We cannot allow our employees to go around assaulting their managers. Therefore ..."

This was it: So long, David!

"... therefore, we have decided that it will be impossible for you to keep your post at Hendle."

I knew it! I just knew it!

"Instead, you and your dolphins will be transferred to our West Coast facility at the earliest opportunity."

What did he say?

"Until your departure, Mr Backhouse will be carrying out his duties at our Welby Park venue, which should prevent any further unpleasantness between you."

I couldn't believe it ...

"Is that acceptable, Mr Capello?"

Acceptable? Was he kidding or what? Not only had I escaped certain dismissal, but I'd also kept hold of Duchess and Herb'e. I found it hard to take in.

Taking a deep breath, I answered. "That's more than acceptable. Please thank the Board for being so understanding."

"Have a little faith," Duchess had said — and she'd been right.

I looked at Dan with a stunned expression before slowly replacing the receiver.

"So? Go on! What happened? What did he say?"

I was in shock — dumbfounded, in fact — but Dan badgered me mercilessly until I'd recounted word for word exactly what I'd been told.

Although overwhelmed by this decision, I was nonetheless acutely aware that Rogers had chosen not to convey the message personally — most probably because he had backed Backhouse and been overruled by the other members of the Board. It was common knowledge that Rogers was a proud man and very much old-school management — not used to being dictated to. Yet, here he was, held to ransom by an employee barely out of his teens — a predicament he'd find hard to swallow.

But he wasn't stupid, and neither were the Board members. They knew that Duchess and Herb'e would refuse to work without me, meaning it was fear — not compassion — that had stayed their hand …

… fear of losing their precious *Perfect Pair.*

This fear had swung the pendulum firmly in my favour, prompting them to break with Company policy — a decision that would have Backhouse literally screaming from the rooftops. Despite all his plotting and all his scheming, his plan had spectacularly backfired. He'd not only failed to get rid of me, but he'd also lost the thing he coveted most — *The Duchess and Flippa Show.*

For a man like Backhouse, this loss of face would be intolerable — a public undermining of his authority that he'd never forget.

And neither would his supporters.

These people had long memories, and they would be quick to pay me back, given the chance. I'd won the battle, but lost the war — not just for me, but for my dolphins too.

I didn't need to be psychic to see what was on the horizon. The events of last night would have the corridors of power muttering …

… muttering that the dream team and their trainer were now a luxury the Company could no longer afford.

⟨ 46 ⟩

The die was cast. It was official.

For better or for worse, on 21st March 1974, my *Perfect Pair* and I were to be evicted from our beloved Hendle and banished to the seaside venue of West Coast – a dolphinarium I'd always despised. In less than one month's time, the three of us would embark on what would be our final journey together.

With Backhouse exiled to Welby, our remaining three weeks' stay should have run smoothly, but, as always, that wasn't the case. One of the reconditioned filters malfunctioned, leading to another farcical three-day shut down for repairs – a situation that sent the pool plummeting back to stagnation.

Clearly aware of my frustration, the engineer tried to explain the problem. "You see, this filtration equipment is so antiquated that no matter how many times you strip it down and tart it up, there'll only ever be so much it can do. Besides, this system was never designed for dolphins. It was meant for people – and that's never gonna change."

I shook my head in resignation. "So you're telling me that even after all this work, these filters will still struggle to handle four dolphins?"

A nasally intake of air, followed by a thoughtful few seconds. "Yeah … that's about it."

Marvellous, bloody marvellous! The last thing Hendle needed. This was especially bad news when bearing in mind Backhouse's controversial wintering policy – the one the Company had so enthusiastically embraced. As always, blinded by the desire to save money, no one at Head Office had even bothered to check whether this obscene scheme would actually work. Hendle was now destined to become an eight-dolphin storage facility; cramped, filthy and destabilised by a water system that couldn't cope – a fiasco that, come winter, the Company would expect *me* to oversee.

I might have been spared dismissal, but how could I possibly participate in a policy I found to be so abhorrent? Be party to such misery?

The answer came as a whisper from that omniscient voice within:

"You won't – neither you nor your dolphins will be around to see it."

clyde rules

❦ 47 ❧

On hearing the news of our forthcoming transfer, the West Coast entertainment complex erupted with excitement. Manager Clive Rothwell, in particular, made no attempt to hide his delight at the thought of securing Europe's top performing dolphins – a far cry from the string of failures he'd been forced to endure since Gerry Mansell's untimely departure. Never in his wildest dreams could Clive have envisaged hosting the famous *Perfect Pair* and, despite our rocky history, he believed this move would herald a bright new start for both of us.

Unfortunately, I didn't share Clive's enthusiasm, because, for me, this relocation would inevitably be painful.

First, it would mean saying goodbye to my lovely landlady, Carla, who'd been like a substitute mum, steering me through the bad times and picking me up when I'd been down. What a gem! She'd made the joys of her home and family my own, and it was unlikely that I'd ever meet her like again.

Second, I'd lose Dan as, for him, a move to West Coast was a bridge too far – although he remained adamant that he would not continue to work under Backhouse at Hendle, meaning that he'd soon be on the dole. A sad waste of talent as this shy and unassuming man had proven his worth many times over.

Another blow would be bidding farewell to my loyal band of volunteers – particularly young Graham, who had been with me since the beginning.

But, without doubt, the most heart-breaking casualties of my moment of madness would be my stolen duo, Baby and Scouse.

With the impending loss of Duchess and Herb'e, Hendle would now demand a replacement team, and these two little dolphins should have been the obvious choice …

… *should* have been, but it seemed that the Company had other ideas.

Since moving to West Coast, blind Scouse had persisted in his work to rule, convincing inept presenters and ignorant managers that he was in some way substandard. Therefore, Head Office – in its infinite wisdom – planned to break up the Baby and Scouse team, returning Baby to Hendle to team up with Eccles and leaving Scouse alone at West Coast.

This was a particularly callous decision because, by taking Baby away, the Company would effectively be tossing Scouse onto the scrapheap.

My poor little prizefighter. Captivity was certainly doing him no favours, no favours at all. From the very first day – when he'd emerged blinded from his traumatic trans-Atlantic transport – he'd seemed cursed.

And now, in robbing him of his friend and guide, the commercial dolphin industry would be stealing his eyesight for a second time.

❧ 48 ☙

Scouse's future certainly looked bleak, as he would be deemed unworthy to partner any of the new dolphins.

However, it was clear to me that any failure to deliver on Scouse's part was down to the fact that none of the West Coast crew knew how to handle him. It should have been obvious to all that he wasn't like any other dolphin. He was blind, so needed specialist treatment: to be precise, thought training – something no one at the seaside venue was capable of implementing.

So, the problem didn't lie with Scouse; the problem lay with the so-called presenters who were supposed to be looking after him. After all, at Hendle, Baby and Scouse had been recognised as a top performing team – the very reason why West Coast had commandeered them in the first place; a heartless managerial decision that I'd never forgotten, nor forgiven, and one that had sent both Scouse and me plummeting down the spiral staircase into depression.

On that fateful day, we had each become tormented souls, lost in a mist of despair from which neither of us had ever truly emerged. Yet, incredibly, the fates were once again pitching us together.

Scouse – the living, breathing enigma; the blinded dolphin who had once been my greatest challenge ...

... a sightless Atlantean whom I was determined to restore to his former glory.

❦ 49 ❧

The Universe was now propelling my dolphins and me along a different path – one that would leave behind our past glories at Hendle. This was a course we had no choice but to follow, brutally heralded by the baleful Backhouse returned to claim back his pool …

… the magnificent Hendle dolphinarium …

… *our* Hendle dolphinarium …

… not only our comfort zone, but also the birthplace of all our success.

This was a bitter pill to swallow.

With my general manager back on the scene, it wasn't long before canvas slings and transport boxes were littering the pool walkways, signalling Duchess and Herb'e's final curtain call at this popular aqua-circus.

"Okay, people, let's not overstay our welcome. Time to go – time to say, 'Bye-bye, Hendle!'"

⟨ 50 ⟩

Predictably, our final catches attracted quite an audience: well-wishers and friends from the safari park and beyond, including young Graham.

"I still can't believe this is happening," he complained. "How could one man have been allowed to cause so much trouble?"

My tearful ally had a point: how indeed? A question mirrored in the reproachful expressions of the two dozen or so dejected onlookers lining the pool safety barriers.

As for our tormentor, Backhouse, as always, had chosen to make himself scarce by burying himself in his office. Today of all days, he didn't intend to face any embarrassing questions. Only on the arrival of Philip Haynes did he surface.

Philip, our playboy vet, was his usual, charming self, chattering amiably as preparations for the transport went ahead. I found it particularly noticeable that he never once referred to the trouble between Backhouse and me – a more than obvious sidestep to avoid any resumption of hostilities.

I afforded myself a wry smirk – this charismatic man never failed to put me at ease, most probably because he was one of the very few people in this business whom I truly respected. Even in those early days, he'd never once questioned my unique *connection* with my dolphins. And now, despite all my problems, it seemed that his faith in me remained steadfast. In fact, I strongly suspected that *he* was the main reason why I still had a job.

"Well, Philip, can't stand here all day chatting, I've got catches to do. After all, we don't want to keep Clive Rothwell waiting."

Leaving Philip to make the final checks, I drifted to the water's edge for one last talk with Duchess and Herb'e.

"Well, you two, this is it. Time to go … so let's have two easy catches, then say our goodbyes."

A warm *connection* – laced with more than a hint of sadness – confirmed that I wasn't telling them anything they didn't already know. There was no doubt that leaving Hendle was going to be a huge wrench for us all.

As for the transport itself, the journey to West Coast was such a short one that it should have been merely a matter of routine.

Alas, it turned out to be anything but, because as Dan and I placed Duchess into her sling, it became immediately apparent that something was wrong.

"Philip, you're not gonna believe this, but the harness is too small. The eye holes don't marry up."

It was obvious that during our stay at Hendle, Duchess had outgrown her original transport sling. An innocuous oversight on our part – but, incredibly, an oversight that would set in motion a series of catastrophic events.

Even now, I ask myself, how could something so trivial have wreaked such devastation?

An outgrown harness … a simple outgrown harness …

… the catalyst for the downfall of me and my beloved *Perfect Pair*.

51

Philip stared intently into Duchess' transport box. "My God, you're right … she's outgrown her harness. When did you last use it?"

Unbelievably, the answer to his question was during the transport from North Liston – well over two and a half years ago. But seeing Duchess every day, I'd never realised just how much she'd grown since then – a fact that would equally apply to Herb'e.

The vet continued to stare thoughtfully into Duchess' box. "Look, Dave, we're already behind schedule as it is, and we don't have time to go hunting around for bigger harnesses. We're just going to have to improvise. After all, it's not as if West Coast is a million miles away. It's a two-hour journey at most, so a couple of minor adjustments should suffice."

Having already witnessed first-hand what damage an inadequate harness could inflict, I was far from convinced. After all, Scouse's shoddy harness had cost him his eyes.

"Philip, that's all well and good for Herb'e, because he's not crated up yet. But Duch is packed and ready to go. I'm gonna have to take her out."

Philip gave a despairing groan before pitching a compromise. "We can't afford to lose any more time. Clive Rothwell and the press are waiting for us at West Coast, and we're late as it is. Besides, removing Duchess from her sling is only going to cause her more distress, so I think it best all round if I make the alterations to her harness with her in it."

Why had Philip's suggestion just triggered my alarm bells?

"With her in it? How are you gonna do that?"

His confident air did little to allay my concerns. "Easy – I'll widen the eye holes with a scalpel. It'll only take a minute."

A shiver ran down my spine.

"A scalpel … a *scalpel*? Philip, are you *sure*?"

❦ 52 ❧

"Dave, I can see by your face that you're not happy with this idea, but, believe me, we just don't have time for anything else. So try not to worry. I know how much Duchess means to you and I promise I'll be very, very careful."

Despite Philip's silky patter and reassuring smile, his effort to convince me fails miserably …

… all he manages to do is send the shriek of alarm bells up a notch.

As he grubs around in his briefcase for a scalpel, I lean over Duchess, hoping to soothe her by catching the light with my ring. But the ring's fire is extinguished by the gloom of the transport box, leaving me little option but to change tactic.

"Don't worry, Duch … not long, now, then we'll be out of here. Just another ten minutes or so, that's all."

My shallow effort to put her at ease isn't working.

"It's okay, Duch, it's okay. Just stay calm … I'm not going anywhere."

Stay calm?

Who am I kidding?

Certainly not me – and definitely not her.

"Please, David, don't let him near me! Please, make him go away!"

I feel it – it snatches at my breath – a jagged *connection* of paralyzing terror, a fear so immediate as to boot me headlong into a psychic blast-off – a quantum leap that detonates a vision from the future.

The fingers of the clock abruptly stop …

… I'm again hanging outside time …

...

... rip ... slip ...

...

... I see the glint of the scalpel ...

...

... rip ... slip ...

...

... I hear the sound of the sawing ...

...

... rip ... slip ...

...

... I see the savagery of the blade ... see it clearly ...

...

... yet how can that be possible?

"Please, David, don't let him near me! You know what will happen!"

Ridiculous. No one can see into the future – no one!

Yet *I* saw it ... I *definitely* saw it ... saw it plainly ...

...

... rip ... slip ...

...

... the glint of the scalpel ...

...

... rip ... slip ...

...

... the tearing of the canvas ...

...

... rip ... slip ...

...

... the pooling of blood.

"Please, David, please, keep him away!"

She's terrified, absolutely terrified. Her screams are penetrating my very core.

What am I gonna do? *What* am I gonna do? My mind's swimming with panic ... can't see, let alone think ... yet I saw it ... I *know* I saw it ...

I catch the flash of the blade in his hand ...

Oh, God! What am I gonna do?

He's Philip – the world-famous vet – a man who doesn't make mistakes…

… yet I saw it … I *definitely* saw it …

A flicker of sun fire and the blade is gone – plunged into the blackness of the box.

Oh, God! God! What am I gonna do? What am I gonna do?

"Please, David, please help me! You know what's going to happen. YOU'VE SEEN IT!"

But this is Philip … Philip! How do I challenge him? How *can* I challenge him? This man doesn't make mistakes … He *doesn't* make mistakes …

Ballistic … my alarm bells are going ballistic … Can hear nothing but a shriek …

… but Philip doesn't make mistakes … he *doesn't* make mistakes …

…

… rip … slip …

…

… deafening …

…

… rip … slip …

…

… excruciating …

…

…rip … slip …

…

Snap out of it, Capello! Snap out of it!

He's not a god … Philip's not a god! He's not infallible … anyone can make a mistake … even him … even *him* …!

…

… rip … slip …

…

"Please, David, please …"

…

… rip … slip …

…

Move … move yourself, Capello … it hasn't happened yet … there's still time!

...

... rip ... slip ...

...

"Please ... PLEASE ..."

...

Time implodes: the fingers of the clock restart.

"I'm coming, Duch, I'm coming ... I won't let you down ... I'm coming ..."

...

... rip ... slip ...

...

... got to protect her ...

...

... rip ... slip ...

...

... got to cover her eye ...

...

... rip ... slip ...

...

... create a shield that the blade can't penetrate ...

...

... rip ... slip ...

...

... a barrier ... got to make a barrier ... got to make it *now*!

...

... rip ... slip ...

...

... rip ... slip ...

...

... my hand ... got to use my hand ...

...

... rip ... slip ...

...

... rip ... slip ...

...

It's done ...

...

... rip ... slip ...

...

... now I wait ... wait for the sting of the blade ...

...

... rip ... slip ...

...

... rip ... slip ...

...

... but my entire being is yelling at me to remove my hand ... remove it now ...

...

... rip ... slip ...

...

... instinct ...

...

... rip ... slip ...

...

... self-preservation ...

...

... rip ... slip ...

...

... ignore the urge, Capello ... grit your teeth and ignore it ...

...

... rip ... slip ...

...

... whatever you do, don't remove your hand ... you *mustn't* remove your ...

...

... rip ...

...

... the sound ...
... *that* sound ...
... the sound from the vision ...
... the sound of tearing canvas.

Is that it? I mean is that really it?

Does that mean I can actually breathe again?

Is it all over or what?

I guess it must be, because I don't feel any pain. In fact, I don't feel anything, anything at all …

… other than a numbing sense of relief.

Makes me wonder what all the fuss was about.

Blimey, me and my imagination! It's about time I learned to get a grip.

What's wrong with Philip? He looks like he's seen a ghost.

"Oh, my God, David!"

Oh, my God, David? What does he mean by that?

What the hell's happened?

What's he seen?

What *isn't* he saying?

For goodness' sake, Philip, give me something more than that, 'cause I'm going off my head here! Come on, say something … open your mouth and say something!

Oh, no! No! I've just had a thought …

… what if the scalpel missed me and plunged into Duchess' head?

Because I still don't feel any pain, still don't feel anything at all.

What if I subconsciously drew back my hand as the blade struck?

Please, *please*, don't let it be! Please tell me I didn't pull away! Please tell me that Duchess is all right – that I didn't let her down!

"Hell's teeth, David! Is Duchess okay?"

Is Duchess okay? Why's he asking me? He's the one who's staring into the box. I mean, I don't know what's happened, do I? I can't bear to even look.

Philip … Philip groaning. Oh, no! Why's he groaning?

"Thank goodness! To think what might have happened – what *would* have happened – if you hadn't been there!"

Hadn't been there … hadn't been there …?

"I might have blinded her …"

Might have … Did he just say *might have* blinded her?

"Come on, David, I need to take a look at that hand of yours, see what damage I've done."

Might have … he definitely said *might* have … That must mean she's okay … Duchess is okay … I didn't let her down, after all … I *didn't* …

"Come on, take that hand out of the box nice and easy."

I can't look … I just can't …

… but I can't help it!

I see it – the shaft of the scalpel glinting in the sunlight …

Aww …! Damn thing's standing upright, it's jammed in so tight … just above the joint of my thumb … Yet I still don't feel any pain …

… weird, totally weird!

"Right, David, I'm going to have to pull that out, so grit your teeth and try not laugh."

Bloody comedian! I suppose he thinks that's funny. Wouldn't be so funny if it were stuck in 'im!

"Right, David, you might want to look away …"

Well, he's not wrong there …

…

Ow!

Ow! Ow! Ow! Ow! *Ow! Ow! Bloody well … Ow!*

"There you go, David – done. Are you okay?"

Just what does he want me to say? Great? Never felt better?

The nit!

"A bit shook-up, Philip, but, otherwise, okay."

Still fibbing, Capello!

"You're losing a lot of blood, David, and that wound's going to need stitches, so I'm afraid it's a trip to the hospital for you."

Hospital – the last thing we need!

"Philip, I can't go to hospital. What about the transport? What about Duchess and Herb'e? We're late as it is."

"Look, David, there isn't going to be a transport without you, because you're the main man."

Ooh! I'm sure Backhouse just winced. He won't like that, won't like that at all! Almost makes it worthwhile.

"Put these overalls over your wetsuit. Can't have you wandering around the hospital half-naked, can we?"

White overalls? Is he kidding or what? I mean *white*? Hardly subtle with all the blood I'm pumping out. Still, can't say anything, 'cause the poor bloke's stressed out as it is. Besides, I've got more important things on my mind – namely, Duchess.

Since that explosive *connection*, she's gone awfully quiet, as if she's purposely shut herself down.

"Duchess, are you okay, girl? Come on, talk to me! Are you okay?"

Nothing. Not a peep. Which means she's hiding.

"Come on, girl, say something, will yer?"

Nothing. She's locked me out.

"David, we haven't got all day. We need to get your hand seen to."

Dammit! I have to go, know I have to go … But I don't want to leave her – not like this.

"David, for goodness' sake! We've got to move!"

"Talk to me, Duch, talk to me! Just say something! Anything!"

"David, what's the hold up? We need to get out of here!"

"Duch …? Duchess …?"

Nothing. Zilch. Nada.

Just an empty silence.

❧ 54 ❧

"Look after Duchess and Herb'e, Dan! Remember to keep dousing them with water – and, whatever you do, don't put them in the back of that transport before I get back! It's freezing out there and the inside of that van is like a fridge. The last thing we need now is another disaster."

Dan nodded anxiously.

"God knows how long I'm gonna be stuck at that hospital, so remember, while I'm getting stitched, Duchess and Herb'e are *your* responsibility."

Philip jostled me towards the door. "Come on, Dave, he knows what to do. Let's get going!"

As the anguished vet bundled me into his car, I was gripped by a profound feeling of anxiety. This wasn't right. Duchess and Herb'e were supposed to be in my care, yet here I was running out on them when they were at their most vulnerable. But Philip was determined, and the car door had barely had time to close before whirling tyres machine-gunned gravel bullets into the air.

"Dan," I shouted, "don't forget what I told you! Keep Duchess and Herb'e inside the pool! Dan, did you hear me …?"

But we were already hurtling towards the main gate, leaving Dan's lone figure in our wake.

"David, keep that towel wrapped tight around your hand. You're bleeding like a pig, and I don't want blood all over my seats."

I nodded, gazing around at the car's lush interior. "Nice car, Philip. Is it new?"

"Yes – cost a fortune."

I could well believe it. The vet's mean machine was truly impressive: a gleaming white top-of-the-range Citroën, suggesting that there was a lot more money to be made in caring for dolphins than in training them. For me, a particularly vexing observation in light of yet another failed pay request.

"Now try not to worry about Duchess and Herb'e," Philip reiterated. The people at Hendle know what they're doing."

Philip's sustained volley of reassurances was wearing thin, because I didn't share his optimism. Dan, although an excellent handler, had no experience in caring for travelling dolphins, and the two-minute crash course I'd delivered was hardly adequate. Plus I was sorely aware that he'd get no support from Backhouse, who would view Duchess and Herb'e as an extension of me – the man he hated – and a symbol of his public humiliation.

I couldn't – and didn't – trust him, so the sooner I got back to Hendle, the better.

❧ 55 ❧

Twenty-five Stirling Moss minutes later saw Philip and me sitting pensively in the packed A&E department of the local hospital, surrounded by horrified onlookers. Hardly surprising – my white overalls resembled the aftermath of a gladiatorial bout. The suit's nylon fabric had acted like a giant sheet of blotting paper, ridiculously exaggerating my loss of blood; a gory sideshow fuelling feverish rumours that I'd been the victim of a crazed dolphin attack – one I'd been lucky to survive.

This unexpected sensationalism catapulted me to the front of the queue, and I couldn't help throwing Philip a sly smirk. "Maybe wearing these white overalls wasn't such a bad idea after all!" No overstatement, because in just over an hour and a half, I was preparing to leave the hospital, proudly sporting six stitches to the base of my thumb – a permanent reminder of my perceived quantum leap.

As customary before discharge, the inevitable instructions on care of the wound followed. "Now this is very important," the attending doctor stressed. "Try not to overwork the hand or there's a chance that you'll split the stitches. And, whatever you do, don't get them wet!"

I gave him a despairing smile. Don't get them wet? Fat chance!

As Philip and I speeded our way back to Hendle, my mind repeatedly trawled those critical moments before the accident.

Just how had I identified that exact moment – the moment when the scalpel would slip?

Equally, how had Duchess?

It was as if we'd been rocketed on a joint journey through time – begging the question, which one of us had initiated it? Me or Duchess? I strongly suspected Duchess.

Infinitely more disturbing, despite my having glimpsed the horror to come, it had still taken Duchess' sheer terror to boot me into action. So why had I hesitated? Why had I fought the vision – a self-doubt that could so easily have ended in disaster?

It was an undisputed fact that I'd always known when Duchess or Herb'e was sick. However, this last supercharged bonding was like nothing I'd experienced before. It had been much more precise. Immediate. *Whoomph!*

When Philip had started sawing at Duchess' sling, my terrified princess had instinctively fled into a psychic retreat – a safe room reserved only for her. But in the throes of her terror, she had forgotten that we were inextricably linked, so had unwittingly dragged me in after her …

… and I do mean dragged.

The theory of just what did actually happen was difficult to formulate because of the speed of events. But I couldn't shake the feeling that I'd inadvertently entered a no-go area – a secret place reserved only for Duchess during times of great stress. And, although she might never repeat her error, she had already unintentionally shown me the path, jolting my mental capacity to another level …

… an awakening of the mind that would pull me even deeper into the dolphin psyche.

❦ 56 ❧

As his gleaming chariot snaked through the winding streets, Philip remained uncharacteristically quiet. I initially put this down to shock, but as time went on, I realised there was something else on his mind.

"I've been thinking, David, no matter how badly things turned out, they could have been a helluva lot worse." The vet's tone was awash with recrimination. "I mean, if not for you, Duchess could have lost an eye … *would* have lost an eye."

I detected the white sheen of his knuckles as he tightened his grip around the steering wheel. "I have to ask: how did you know that the scalpel would slip? How could you be so sure?"

It seemed that my intuition had not gone unnoticed.

"Your hand must have been in position even as the canvas tore, because no one has reflexes that quick. So how did you know?"

I smiled. "You're gonna find this hard to believe, Philip. I knew because Duchess told me, or – to be more exact – showed me."

An uncomfortable few seconds followed as he struggled to digest my response. "Showed you? How do you mean, showed you?"

Had it been anyone else asking this question, I would have answered with greater caution. However, to me, this man was special – visionary.

"It's difficult to explain. Call it a revelation … a flash from the future … whatever you want. But – whatever you call it – it came from Duchess. That might sound crazy, but I don't know any other way to put it. I saw that scalpel slip – saw it clear as day."

Philip nodded, but passed no comment. This cultured individual had known me far too long to simply rubbish my explanation, no matter how far-fetched it might seem. He had always been one of the few men never to doubt the psychic bond existing between me and my dolphins.

What he would have struggled to believe, however, was how my almost nonchalant ability to access the dolphin radio was now presenting me with new gifts, new opportunities – most notably the power to wander. Those barred doors to the inner sanctums of the dolphin mansion were beginning to open one by one, granting me an even deeper understanding of my Atlantean friends, who were much closer to possessing a soul than the majority of humankind would care to admit. A dangerous concept that could all too easily upset the architecture of the evolutionary pyramid – an outdated paradigm that the self-proclaimed master race would always fiercely protect. Although profoundly flawed, this dubious structure would forever see these proud people of the sea suffering beneath man's yolk.

"We're nearly there, David," Philip interjected, "so we'll have to be quick off the mark. We're a full two and a half hours behind schedule."

Saved by the bell – this line of thinking was getting way too deep. Plus, I had to get my mind in gear and back to the job at hand.

"Yeah, you're right Philip. We've lost enough time as it is, so let's get this show on the road."

West Coast here we come – at last!

⫷ 57 ⫸

On arriving at Hendle, I was horrified to find my *Perfect Pair* packed and waiting in the back of an ice-cold transport van – profoundly disturbing, as I'd left strict instructions that they should remain in the warmth of the dolphinarium.

"Dan, what the hell's going on? I particularly stressed that Duchess and Herb'e were not to leave the building until I got back, so do you mind telling me what they're doing in that bloody fridge?"

My distressed colleague was quick to fill me in with the details. "I didn't have a choice, David. I was overruled. Backhouse insisted that we load them up. He said he didn't want you or your dolphins at Hendle for a moment longer than necessary."

I was livid. Backhouse had been well aware of my instructions, yet had blatantly chosen to disregard them, reaffirming that the sooner my team and I got away from him the better.

"How long have they been in there?" I snapped.

Dan replied sheepishly. "A good two hours."

I felt my jaw tighten. Two hours … a full two hours …

"Right, David!" It was Philip. "Tommy's got them all packed and ready to go for us, so it looks like we're on our way."

It was obvious by the vet's jubilant mood that he viewed Backhouse's "helping hand" as a bonus, which meant I couldn't really kick up a fuss; but, to this day, I'd prefer to think that even a man like Backhouse couldn't have predicted the terrible ramifications of his actions.

His "helping hand" would effectively initiate the collapse of our dynasty. My *Perfect Pair* would never be the same again.

116

ᕗ 58 ᕘ

I've no option but to bid a hasty farewell to Dan and young Graham, because Philip's revving the living daylights out of his car – a less than subtle reminder that he wants us to get going.

Rushing, rushing, always soddin' rushing. And for what? I mean, if Philip hadn't been in such an all-fire hurry in the first place, none of this would have happened: I wouldn't have ended up in hospital, and Duchess and Herb'e wouldn't have been freezing their tails off for over two hours in those damn slings.

God! Two hours … two full hours …

Hard to believe, especially when you consider that the whole trip should have been done and dusted in much the same time.

Well, too late for recriminations now – the wheels are whirling and we're on our way.

As usual, Philip's following behind, just in case anything goes wrong. (Goes wrong? That's a joke, because so far today nothing's gone right!) But at least he's travelling alone, which means that Head Office must have given orders for Backhouse to remain at Hendle. A right smack in the teeth for him, because he relishes these press calls – loves playing the big shot and posing for the cameras. Well, he won't be posing this time – no sir! – *he's* definitely in the bad books. What a humiliation! What an utter humiliation! Still, if anyone deserves it, he does.

Even so, there's no point getting cocky. Backhouse won't forget this in a hurry, and neither will his mates. They'll be eager to pay me back, sooner rather than later. These people aren't the sorts to forgive and forget – the lousy, rotten sods.

Anyway, can't fret about them – got enough on my plate with Duchess and Herb'e. Neither one of them has moved a muscle since we set off, which isn't a good sign. I clearly remember our last journey from North Liston, how the two of them had never stopped chattering – so much so that I could actually feel the air sparking electricity. A fantastic experience – nothing like the one we're having now. No question, this transport is different, totally different. The shutdown I sensed earlier with Duchess seems to have spread to Herb'e, and the dolphin radio is as dead as a dodo.

What a rotten, horrible day. How could it all have gone so wrong?

And just to top it off, my hand hurts … hurts like hell.

❦ 59 ❧

The three of us are like lost souls drowning in our own silence. Practically a replay of the last time I ended up trekking to this God-forsaken place, when forced to surrender Baby and Scouse to the West Coast Management. In fact, the whole trip is nothing short of déjà-vu: that same windowless box, that same eerie atmosphere – meticulously bound by a gnawing feeling of foreboding.

And now, even the sounds filtering through the van walls – meaning we're getting close, close to our destination.

Thank goodness!

Just listen to that din – even though it's officially off-season, there's a cacophony of shrieks, wails and whistles blasting from the multitude of neon highwaymen lining the West Coast promenade, peppered by the inane laughter of a few early-bird thrill seekers.

People … I'm really beginning to detest them – especially those that wear suits and work at Head Office.

"Okay, my beauties, we're nearly there. Better late than never."

Not a sound. Not so much as a squeak.

"Aww, come on, you two. Nothing to worry about now."

Did I just say "nothing to worry about"? I can't help but wonder, was that remark for their benefit or mine?

I have an awful feeling it was for mine.

❧ 60 ❧

A shriek of brakes as the transport's metal ribs shuddered to a halt – we'd paused at the traffic lights that would direct us to the rear of the seaside dolphinarium. With no windows through which to view the outside world, I cocked my head to listen, but could discern little above the manic glee of the sinister laughing clown – a grotesque Victorian sentinel that guarded the entrance to the Fun City amusement park. I shuddered as I pictured his twisted features. Little wonder he was so jubilant: this mechanical monstrosity had cheated death many times – the sole survivor of a bygone age. Unfortunately, I'd be seeing and hearing a lot more of him once I'd settled in.

Within fifteen minutes of our arrival, my subdued pair and I were exploring our new pool and reacquainting ourselves with an old mate – one we hadn't seen for some time – Scouse.

My never-forgotten hero showed his pleasure by racing around the pool in joyous abandonment. It was certainly great to see him again, because – heaven knows! – I'd missed him. For me, this blind dolphin had always been a beacon in the darkness, emitting a radiant pick-me-up – a cruelly ironic gift bestowed by fate on a luckless Atlantean who'd been robbed of his own sight.

"Good old Scouse! You lovely, lovely fella!"

Lifting my eyes from the mirror, I suddenly became aware of a lone figure silently watching me from the opposite side of the pool. It was the diminutive form of Clive Rothwell, the West Coast manager. As our gazes met, I vividly recalled our last meeting: that dark day of Baby and Scouse's commandeering. I remembered how he'd offered his hand in friendship – a gesture I'd thrown back in his face.

Now, however, things were different, and when he beamed me a warm smile and again stretched out his hand, I accepted it with enthusiasm.

"Good to have you and your team here, David. I can't tell you just how proud I am. I'm sure we'll work well together."

The warmth of Rothwell's animated greeting suggested that my prizefighter's inner light was more than a little contagious.

"Thanks, Clive, good to be here …"

… I lied.

❦ 61 ❧

The following day buzzed with excitement as managers, fairground workers and artistes from the adjoining Tennessean Show Bar filed into the dolphinarium to sneak a peek at my prize dolphins. My dynamic duo's lofty reputation had drawn them out in their hordes – a PR opportunity I seized upon in an attempt to repair the damage I'd caused during my last visit. So there were plenty of smiling faces as Clive Rothwell showed us off to the local dignitaries and introduced us to the dolphinarium staff.

My new presenters all appeared enthusiastic, although none of them boasted any experience of working with dolphins – the very reason why this seaside venue had suffered so badly in the past. There was no doubt that I'd need to educate them if I intended to make my stay here a success.

As strange as it might seem, since our arrival, I'd had little chance to concentrate on what mattered most – my *Perfect Pair*. Since their release into the pool, Duchess and Herb'e hadn't eaten a thing. Moreover, they'd remained uncharacteristically aloof, shunning the lavish attentions of their many admirers. I was particularly concerned about Herb'e, who'd maintained that same state of shutdown so evident during the transport. At first, I tried to attribute my anxiety to an overactive imagination, but by noon, he was still swimming aimlessly around the pool and refusing to come into the stage.

And as the day drifted on, my alarm bells rang even louder. Although early days, Herb'e's behaviour now bore all the trappings of a dolphin mind-set – a mental lockout I'd prayed never to see again. I'd witnessed this cursed condition many times in the pens of North Liston (most notably when dealing with the tragic Bubbles), and I knew all too well what it was capable of, meaning I'd have to monitor both my dolphins closely.

"Come on, you two, what's wrong? What's with the silent treatment?"

Nothing from Herb'e, but Duchess replied with a thunderous blast of air and an angry bout of tail slapping, before deliberately turning her back on me.

"Blimey, Duchess, you've got a right cob on. It wasn't my fault I had to leave you. I had no choice … I mean, for God's sake, I had a scalpel stuck in my hand."

The silence of her *connection* was deafening – she had barred all doors. Nevertheless, her tantrum was at least encouraging, because it showed that she'd begrudgingly switched her radio back on – something that couldn't be said for Herb'e.

The situation was becoming seriously unnerving. This behaviour was in stark contrast to their normally bubbly displays of excitement. Something was wrong – terribly wrong.

Closing my eyes, I struggled to search for Herb'e's song, but instead found myself mugged by a familiar diamond-tipped *connection*.

"Come on, Dave, when are we gonna work? When? When? When?"

Bang!

There was no mistaking the euphoric Scouse – the blind Atlantean Management had been so quick to cast aside.

"Well, Scouse, I'm glad someone's happy to see me. How are you doing, my son?"

Whatever Duchess and Herb'e's problems, they certainly didn't extend to my prizefighter – all doors to his mind were open wide.

"I can't believe you're here, David … I still can't believe you're here!" he gabbled, trailing me along the side of the stage. *"So when do we start work? When?"*

It was amazing – no matter what life threw at him, this little dolphin's boundless enthusiasm always managed to shine through.

"Can't start work yet, Scouse. Got a lot to do. But it won't be long … I promise, it won't be long …"

The poor fella was gagging to make up for lost time, but even *his* infectious drive couldn't galvanise me into action. I only had one thing on my mind …

… Herb'e.

⟨ 62 ⟩

That evening, during our customary playtime, Duchess and Herb'e confirmed all my misgivings by constantly swimming just out of reach. Duchess, fuming about the perceived indignities she'd had to endure during the transport, continued to transmit a hostile *connection*, whereas Herb'e remained barricaded within his secret hideaway.

"*Ohhh, come on, you two! How long are you gonna keep this up? You can't keep blaming me … You know what happened.*"

The cold shoulder treatment showed no signs of abating.

"*Right, if that's the way you feel, stuff it! Playtime's over – I'm gone!*"

With them in this mood, there was no point in hanging around. My two dolphins had made it abundantly clear just whom they held responsible for their present woes, and I was definitely *persona non grata*. So, dragging myself from unwelcome waters, I miserably headed for the shower.

I'd never before known behaviour like this – especially not from Duchess, who would normally swim through hot coals for me. So *what* had brought about this change? What had gone wrong – besides the obvious?

Had something else happened to my dolphins … something of which I wasn't aware?

❦ 63 ❧

I already knew that, against my instructions, my dolphins had been taken from a warm dolphinarium and dumped in a freezing cold van; knew that they'd been left frightened and alone for God knows how long. But what I didn't know was whether anything else untoward had happened.

My brain was squirming with conspiracy theories impossible to substantiate. The only thing I could be sure of was how Duchess and Herb'e were feeling now. They felt betrayed, and blamed me for not being there when they'd been vulnerable – a bitter accusation I couldn't refute because, in my heart of hearts, no matter what the circumstances, I knew I should never have left them.

For years, Duchess and Herb'e had been my responsibility, my babies, yet I'd allowed myself to be derailed from my duty of care …

… if only I could turn back the clock.

We'd been at West Coast for barely two days and already my team and I were succumbing to the curse of this wretched pool – a stricken dolphinarium from which we had no escape.

⤷ 64 ⤶

Logbook entry 22nd March 1974: Herb'e is looking well, but still seems upset with himself and hasn't yet eaten … Perhaps it's all happening a little too fast for everybody.

Who are you kidding, Capello? You wrote this starry-eyed bullshit a full three days ago, trying to convince yourself that everything would be okay. But it's not okay: Herb'e's still not eating – further proof, if ever you needed it, that your inbuilt alarm system rarely gets it wrong, and it's more fool you for trying to ignore it.

That dreaded mind-set – the one you so fear – now looks closer and closer to becoming a reality, which means you can't hold off any longer. You've got to call the vet.

God, what are you gonna tell Clive Rothwell?

At least Duchess is eating again, even if it *is* only bits and pieces. Better still, she's kicked off working – albeit without Herb'e, which is disappointing. Still, you should be thankful for small mercies, because the last thing you need right now is a joint hunger strike.

On the bright side, the West Coast season hasn't officially started yet, so Management aren't pushing for shows. But that won't last long, and, if things don't improve, you could well find yourself opening with a one-dolphin show – a one-dolphin show with a blind dolphin with no guide.

God! Now you *have* to call the vet – and pronto!

Let's face it, you've got two sick dolphins, and you're running out of time. What *are* you gonna tell Clive Rothwell?

⋊ 65 ⋉

That night, I found it impossible to sleep, my mind probing for reasons why Herb'e wouldn't eat. Yet, no matter how hard I tried, I found it impossible to tear my thoughts from that fateful transport. Maybe it was my psyche trying to appease my guilty conscience, but I couldn't shake the feeling that, whilst I was at hospital, something sinister had happened in the back of that van.

It was true that my dolphins had given me many anxious nights in the past, but never like this. My dreamscape was laced with night terrors – fragmented images of the horrors of North Liston. And, even worse, I felt certain that this dark canvas of hazy recollections would soon be manifesting itself into my waking reality.

Next morning, I traipsed wearily along the deserted promenade, wishing I might be anywhere but in this bleak seaside town.

"God, I hate this bloody miserable place. What the hell are we doing here? I mean, *what*? We should be home at Hendle where we belong … not languishing in this rotten hole."

Drowning in self-recrimination, I tried to manipulate the blame game – but, deep down, I knew that *I* was the *real* reason we were stuck here. The night I'd challenged Backhouse was the night I'd condemned my team and myself into exile. That perceived victory against my general manager had been nothing but a sham. All I'd done was propel those I loved most down the road to oblivion. Some leader I'd turned out to be. Not only had I lost the battle, I'd also lost the war – big time.

On reaching the dolphinarium, I paused apprehensively before turning the key.

"Please, if you two can hear me, please make things right. Please make everything the way it was before the transport. Please … please …"

127

❦ 66 ❧

I walk on stage, hardly daring to breathe, let alone look. Peering into a mirror that will never be my own, I scan its alien plane for signs of illness and cock my head to interpret its early-morning whisper … watching, listening.

A dank fog hangs over the arena like a shroud, coating my face with a film of stinging condensation.

"Come on, people, talk to me, for God's sake … Tell me what's wrong …"

Watching, listening …

Instinctively, I breathe in, but not out …

Waiting, waiting …

An echo …

… only an echo – the eerie sound of blowholes pushing air around the deserted dolphinarium.

I dither despondently, almost ready to turn back towards the kitchen … then, from the corner of my eye, I see it – a green veil of vomit skulking in the shadows of a distant pool sump …

… and where there's one veil, there has to be more, so I look harder …

… there! to my right – directly to my right – another nebula of bile circling a sump grill …

… and now to my left – yet another in the confines of the holding pen …

… far too much vomit for just one dolphin …

… Duchess and Herb'e's condition has worsened overnight.

"Come on, you two, come into the side so I can check you out."

They still won't comply, deliberately keeping their distance from the stage.

Nevertheless, it's impossible not to clock the stream of diarrhoea now billowing from Herb'e's rear.

I've seen enough – I need a vet, and I need one fast.

Philip's already aware of the situation, because I called him last night, but, like an idiot, I forgot to ask what time he'd be here. I need to hurry him up, because I can't afford any more delays. So it's back down those grey slab steps to the kitchen and the telephone.

The West Coast kitchen – miniscule compared to Hendle's, and situated just below the pool, meaning it's constantly dark and clammy. More reminiscent of a cave than a restroom.

As I hang on the line, I can't help but notice the mermaid's scales clinging to the kitchen walls – a glinting shawl reminding me that nothing in this horrible place ever escapes the nymph from the mirror. Tables, chairs, worktops, all painted in a paper-thin layer of glistening salt. Even the telephone receiver seems to ooze a cold sweat.

Tentatively, I wait for the ringtone to cease, then …

… NO! NO! NO!

This can't be happening! I'm being diverted – my emergency call to Philip is being diverted! The question is, diverted to where?

The line clicks, and I immediately recognise the deadpan voice of Philip's partner, Tony Forrester. That's all I need – the last time I dealt with Forrester, I blackmailed him into authorising a Hendle pool dump during peak season, which means that this conversation is going to be sticky to say the least.

"Sorry, David, I'm afraid Philip's been called abroad on an emergency and won't be back for at least five days."

Great! Fantastic! Five full days! But *I* can't wait five full days, because Philip's not the only one who has an emergency.

"Anyway, what's so pressing that you have to rob me of my beauty sleep?"

Beauty sleep? I'd hardly go that far …

"Well, Tony, it's Herb'e … Well, not just Herb'e … Duchess too … But Herb'e more …"

Just listen to me – I sound like a blithering idiot who can't string a sentence together.

"Sorry, Tony, I've not had much sleep, so I'll start again. Duchess and Herb'e are both sick, and I'm pretty sure it's down to the transport. I'm particularly worried about Herb'e … he hasn't eaten a thing since he arrived here and every part of me is screaming, 'Serious!'"

I hang onto his silence.

"Okay, David, I'm a good three hours away, so give me chance to have a quick shower and a bite to eat, then I'll be on my way."

It's strange how a crisis can build bridges. My blackmailing tactics must still be fresh in Forrester's mind, yet his attitude was not only professional, but also verging on friendly. And whilst he's certainly no Philip, I can't help but wonder if I didn't get this bloke wrong last time we met. After all, it wouldn't be the first time – and it won't be the last.

Still, this isn't about joining the Tony Forrester Fan Club; it's about getting a job done …

… it's about saving Herb'e.

And I do mean *saving*.

❦ 67 ❧

Whilst waiting for the vet, I again tried to tempt Duchess and Herb'e to eat. Herb'e, in particular, was now showing all the physical signs of five torturous days without food, his three double chins all but gone and that dreaded dip behind his head evident for all to see. And Duchess wasn't far behind him, her food intake having plummeted to such a degree that she too could no longer maintain her body weight.

My greatest fear had materialised – the initiation of the corruptive dolphin mind-set. I likened this condition to a mind merge where one Atlantean psyche strongly influenced the other – a mutually agreed brainwashing that virtually always ended in disaster. I'd been here before, so didn't need a crystal ball to know what was coming next: catches – constant catches – and those inevitable, horrendous force-feeds.

I had to accept that desperate times lay ahead. The stakes literally couldn't be higher, which meant I'd have to prepare myself mentally for the unthinkable …

… the unthinkable …

…

… I *couldn't* lose my *Perfect Pair* … I just couldn't.

❧ 68 ❧

Unlike Hendle, the West Coast dolphinarium had only one holding pen, which was, in itself, inadequate. But, fortunately for me, it boasted a false floor made of canvas – something that would render those strenuous open water catches a thing of the past.

This false floor had a spring-based metal skeleton attached to a series of ropes and pulleys, which meant it could be raised manually. On the downside, however, the added weight made it extremely heavy, meaning I'd need plenty of muscle on hand. Thankfully, this wasn't a problem, as being virtually next door to Fun City meant I had an abundance of burly fairground workers to call on – an embarrassment of manpower that I'd never been afforded at Hendle.

The canvas base, when in operation, acted much like a giant umbrella, only in reverse. An ingenious contraption birthed as a direct result of Backhouse's twisted policy – a much-needed aid to compensate for a pool where no one could train and no one could catch. In other words, a pool that had never recovered from the loss of its trainer, my one-time friend and mentor, Gerry Mansell.

Gerry Mansell … how I needed him now!

Fascinating, the machinations of the human mind: when thinking of Gerry, I recalled nothing of the good times we'd shared, but only his haunting caveat: "Remember, dolphinariums don't just break dolphins, they break people too."

Particularly fitting now as my greatest fear edged ever closer: the resumption of the North Liston syndrome. A gut-wrenching scenario that was now threatening to replay here …

… here in this wretched seaside town of West Coast.

❦ 69 ❧

By early afternoon, Forrester had blood tested both Duchess and Herb'e and administered injections of antibiotics and multivitamins – crucial treatments to tide them over whilst waiting for their all-important blood results.

"Well, David, until I know exactly what we're dealing with, that's all I can do. But I have a strange feeling that their illness is down to a waterborne virus."

Personally, I didn't agree. I was certain that all our troubles had stemmed from that catastrophic transport.

"I don't think so, Tony. If it were down to the water, Scouse would be ill too, which he's not. In fact, if truth be known, Scouse is bouncing out of his skin, so it *can't* be down to the water."

Forrester accepted my challenging his diagnosis with a wry smirk. "Look, David, it's pure speculation on my part, because I can't be sure of anything until I get those bloods analysed."

He was spot on – nothing was certain, which meant that time was of the essence and I couldn't take any chances. "Right," I said decisively, "tonight I'm gonna seal my dolphins in the holding pen and blast the main pool with a high dose of chlorine. That way, if there's anything sinister in there, the chemical blitz should burn it away."

Forrester frowned. "There's not much room in that pen for three dolphins. They'll barely be able to turn around."

He wasn't wrong there – my poor Atlanteans would hardly be able to move, let alone swim – but it had to be done. If the water did indeed hold something untoward, I had to get rid of it, and fast.

"I know it's not gonna be much fun for them, but it won't be a barrel of laughs for me, either. I've hardly slept a wink since I arrived in this bloody awful place, so the last thing I need right now is the added pressure of an all-night pool blitz. But, the way things are panning out, I literally have no other choice."

The vet didn't respond. At first, I interpreted his silence as a sign of disagreement, but following his gaze, I soon realised my mistake.

"You do realise that both your dolphins are losing weight rapidly, don't you?" he observed.

Losing weight? That was an understatement … I knew all right.

"You're soon going to have to consider force-feeding."

My heart plummeted at the very mention of the words …

… force-feeding …

… a trainer's nightmare …

… *this* trainer's nightmare.

However, Forrester had merely put into words what I already knew, and I couldn't stick my head in the sand any longer.

"Okay, Tony," I sighed, "by my reckoning it should take twelve hours to shock the pool and at least another twelve to get those blood results, which gives me less than two days to get things back on track. If it turns out that the water isn't the culprit – and I don't think it is – then we'll have to go for force-feeds."

Forrester's expression barely changed. "Fair enough, I'll go along with that. They're your charges, so it's your call, but we can't wait too long."

I found it impossible to stay positive. In my heart of hearts, I knew that Duchess and Herb'e's woes had nothing to do with the water, which meant that in just twenty-four hours' time – no matter how abhorrent – the horror of twin force-feeds would start again.

❧ 70 ❧

A blurry twelve hours had elapsed before the water readings had normalised sufficiently for me to release my three distressed dolphins.

The water looked magnificent: the mirror's rejuvenated face glinted beneath the sunlight, sparking the dance of a billion photon fairies, vibrant beings attesting to the success of my shock and awe treatment. Yet, spectacular as it now looked, I'd always known that the water had never been the problem. After all, we'd been forced to endure far worse at Hendle – a sobering reflection that again left me pointing the finger of suspicion at that disastrous transport.

Nevertheless, any success in treating the water had come too late to influence my decision about force-feeding: I was now fully committed to going down the road I'd fought so hard to avoid.

"Tony, the pool's been shocked and the water readings are fine. That means the force-feeds are on, so I'll need you back here at West Coast ASAP." I became conscious of my fingers cramping around the telephone receiver.

"I think you've made the right decision, David. The sooner we start the feeds, the better," the vet replied. "I've just received Duchess' and Herb'e's blood results, and we've got big trouble. By the way, you were right about the water – that wasn't the culprit. Both dolphins are suffering from a severe chill, most likely exacerbated by the stress of the delayed transport."

I grimaced. Never mind stress, I thought, more like the two hours plus they'd spent languishing in the back of a freezing cold van – a farewell gift courtesy of Backhouse.

"And there's more …"

I held my breath.

"Herb'e is causing particular concern. On top of the chill, his blood is showing anaemia and a serious infection of unknown origin. In other words, he's a very sick dolphin ... a very, very sick dolphin. I'm afraid he's going to need daily injections of antibiotics and multivitamins – treatments that will be ongoing for some considerable time."

With my worst fears confirmed, I found myself lost for words.

"On a brighter note," he continued, "apart from a severe chill, Duchess' test results haven't shown anything serious, which leaves me wondering why she's not eating."

Forrester might be a first-class vet, but he knew nothing of the dolphin psyche. As I feared, Duchess had joined Herb'e in a destructive mind-set – a burgeoning suicide pact that, if not broken, would drag them both to disaster.

In supporting Herb'e, Duchess had cut herself off from everyone and everything – including me – electing to withdraw into one of those hidden rooms where it was impossible to engage her.

It was true that Duchess had refused to speak since her terrifying ordeal with the scalpel, yet without her song, it was impossible for me to intervene. Her *connection* was the mother *connection*, and without it, there could be only one outcome ...

... an outcome too unbearable to even contemplate.

❧ 71 ❧

I stand on this unforgiving stage, my eyes drawn into the watery pit. As always, an early morning veil hangs motionless across its face, and I can't help thinking how eerie it looks. It's like standing on another planet.

What a depressive, soulless place a dolphinarium can be when things are going wrong. Come to think of it, what a depressive, soulless place a dolphinarium can be when things are going right. Nothing, literally nothing, escapes the misery of the penetrating damp. Everything wears a liquid film, including me, and I've only been in the place for fifteen minutes – a lone, pathetic figure praying for a miracle.

A sudden snort reminds me why I'm here so early in the morning: dolphins – three dolphins sleeping, three dolphins schooling. Unfortunately, two of them sick and minus that all-important *connection*.

It's amazing. Even after all this time, I can't help but marvel at the grace with which they weave the water – that effortless roll, reminiscent of a silk scarf floating in a soft breeze.

I wonder … do they know what's coming? Do Duchess and Herb'e have any idea of the horror that's about to be visited on them? Or have they drifted so far away that they no longer care?

Like me, they're prisoners of the mirror … the *enchanted* mirror … *my* enchanted mirror …

… nothing more than an over-sized concrete box.

What a rotten, horrible, horrible existence – three beautiful people trapped forever in an alien world.

And for what?

Their smile, their generous smile – a feature that remains fixed even when they cry.

What a terrible price to pay for simply looking happy.

God, I'm dreading today, I really am. Anyway, can't stand around moping. Got things to do.

They haven't stirred. Do I wake them or what?

No, I'll leave 'em … No need to wake them yet. Forrester won't be here for at least another hour, so I can allow them their dreams of freedom for a little while longer …

… after all, with what they've got coming, that's the least I can do.

❦ 72 ❧

"Sorry I'm late, David. The traffic on the motorway was murder … I think there must have been an accident." Forrester looked flustered. "Have they eaten anything yet?"

"No, neither Duchess nor Herb'e has taken a single bite."

"What about Scouse? How's he bearing up?"

The vet was obviously anxious that my little prizefighter might join the ranks of the hunger strikers.

"Scouse is all right – you don't have to worry about him. You won't catch him being drawn into any dolphin mind-set. He's a loner, a real survivor. We had a similar situation to this back in the old days of North Liston. A dolphin called Bubbles … Never took a fish whilst in captivity … well, not willingly, anyway. Poor girl went through weeks of force-feeds … It was terrible. But even her weakened state didn't stop her calling to the other dolphins, trying to seduce them into refusing food. First Duchess and Herb'e succumbed … then Stumpy … and, finally, Baby. Bubbles' call was like a cancer. I thought we were gonna lose them all – all, that is, except Scouse." I offered the vet a reassuring smile. "No, you definitely don't have to worry about Scouse. He's a one-off."

Suddenly, a young presenter stepped from the shadows carrying two loaded fish buckets – a sobering reminder of what was about to happen.

As Forrester made his way towards the pen, she turned to me. "What was wrong with Bubbles? Why wouldn't she eat?"

I cringed – she'd obviously been earwigging.

Bubbles … What could I say about Bubbles …?

❦ 73 ❧

"Well, looking at Bubbles, she appeared to be a perfect dolphin specimen; but that was on the outside. On the inside, it was an altogether different story. The poor girl's mind was seriously messed up – broken, in fact. She'd never recovered from the trauma of being captured, and had completely shut herself down. She was lost in a typical dolphin mind-set, and, no matter how hard we tried, we couldn't bring her back."

The wide-eyed presenter listened thoughtfully, before asking, "What's a dolphin mind-set? I've never heard of it before."

"A dolphin mind-set? It's difficult to explain. I guess you could say it's a complete mental withdrawal that happens when a dolphin can't take the stress any longer."

She still looked puzzled.

"Okay," I continued, "imagine that you've just had a blinding row with your mum and dad, and you're so angry that you can't stand to be in the same room with them anymore. What do you do? You run upstairs, lock yourself in your bedroom and hide the key. In other words, you shut them – and everyone else – out. You use your room as a fortress where no one can get to you. Let's face it, we've all been there at one time or other.

"But ask yourself this? What happens if the outside world so revolts you that you decide *never* to leave your room again? What happens if you stay there for so long that you actually forget where you hid the key? That room then becomes a prison of your own making – a cell from which there's no escape. Now does that make sense?"

She nodded uncertainly, which meant it probably didn't.

140

"So in the end, what happened to Bubbles?"

This girl had no intention of letting me off the hook.

"Well, eventually, she committed suicide. Killed herself. And as sad as that sounds, that's pretty much the story. Believe me, in those early days, the North Liston pens were a horrible place to be."

Committed suicide … something I'd never questioned – until recently – because what I'd neglected to mention were the disturbing rumours that were now openly circulating on the dolphin grapevine. The wire was rife with talk of "throwaway dolphins", troublesome Atlanteans callously despatched because they were deemed unable to earn their keep. If this were indeed true, it would almost certainly apply to the purging of the mentally or physically sick – a covert practice that would be frighteningly easy to accomplish.

The vulnerability of the dolphin's blowhole would offer the easiest option, as any foreign body blocking this vital airway would prove fatal.

We'd all heard the stories about coins being thrown into the show arenas by an ignorant public – a practice that proved all too convenient when it came to pointing the finger of blame.

But there was another way – far, far more devious. Every established trainer had heard whisper of it: the invisible killer – a glob of grease, transparent and childishly easy to handle. This obstruction could be hidden in the palm, before being surreptitiously slipped into the blowhole of any unwanted dolphin, allowing the perpetrator time to sneak away, leaving the doomed Atlantean to suffocate alone.

This horrific act of murder would be impossible to detect by those insurance companies obliged to pay out large sums of money on the death of a show dolphin.

Just where these ghastly tales had originated from, I didn't know, but I strongly suspected disillusioned and bitter ex-pen trainers. Even so, knowing how cruel and secretive this business could be, I couldn't just rubbish them. These rumours had to have substance, which threw up an even more harrowing question: did an atrocity such as this happen on my watch?

I'd be the first to admit that Bubbles' death had proved to be very fortuitous for us all – particularly in light of her passing less than two weeks before we were due to ship out to our respective pools. I was also aware that the last thing any of us needed at that time was a suicidal dolphin to blight the opening shows. So, no matter how repugnant, the question had to be asked: was Bubbles a throwaway dolphin?

If she were, it would quite literally mean that all the people I'd ever worked with now fell under a cloak of suspicion – an alarming indictment of friends and colleagues working in an industry not known for giving out answers.

Still, no matter how disturbing this line of thought might be, I couldn't afford to get tangled up with any more conspiracy theories. It was imperative that I stay focussed. I had a job to do – one that couldn't be put off any longer.

Damn bloody force-feeds … I hate them … hate them …

❦ 74 ❧

"I'm sorry, Duchess, I'm so sorry, but I have to do this ... There isn't any other way ..."

A psychic message that sounded like an antiquated recording, replaying virtually word for word what I'd said to her all those years ago back in North Liston. Even my actions were the same as I flashed my ring at the sun in a pathetic attempt to give her comfort.

Some comfort ...!

... rough handling ... disinfected gags ... a mound of strangers pinning her down ...

... and worst of all, vivacious blue eyes morphing into grey pearls.

Horrible! Utterly soul-destroying! Bloody force-feeds ... Bloody, bloody, rotten force-feeds!

Thank God they're over. Thank God they're done. Nothing more to do now but wait, wait and pray that my dolphins' ordeals will have the desired effect of shocking them into taking food.

The desired effect ...

Man! I've had it up to here with this constant worry. I've been living in this rotten filthy gaff for over a week, and I need a serious change of scenery – need it fast. Maybe go check out the nearest amusement arcade. Put the skills of a misspent youth to the test. Get normalised.

Weird ... still can't get used to an out-of-season resort. What a dead-end place – promenade deserted and arcades virtually empty. There's hardly a soul around. In fact, the whole town is in an enforced hibernation. Eerie ... decidedly creepy.

Whoa! Hold on! Wait a minute! Stop the show! Just look at that! A long-legged beauty lounging in the corner of that arcade – and, even better, she's all alone. Maybe things are looking up.

Can't imagine why you're hiding in the shadows, gorgeous, because you're definitely the best thing I've seen since arriving in this rotten, depressive hole. Better get my skates on, because, looking the way you do, you won't be on your lonesome for very long.

So, here goes nothing …

"*Hello*, beautiful, what's your name?"

75

The leggy temptress brazenly flashed her name before me: *The Killer Babe from Outer Space*. Awestruck, I snatched a deep breath as I basked in the presence of the most magnificent pinball machine I'd ever seen. I felt my heart pounding as I succumbed to her cosmic advances, intergalactic come-ons that immediately flicked the switch of my obsessive need to always be the best – a deep-rooted compulsion that soon manifested itself in the racking-up of multiple free games.

My resurrected skills quickly brought me to the attention of my fellow pinball enthusiasts, as well as a less-than-amiable arcade manager.

"You're not half-bad on that machine. Just make sure you play off all those games before you leave, because it's bad enough trying to make a living during the low season as it is."

The *thwack* of diminishing profits had obviously hit a raw nerve.

"Anyway, enjoy it while you can," he sneered, "'cause when the season starts, you've got no chance."

Body still glued to my neon lover, but concentration broken, I couldn't resist a cocky parry. "What d'yer mean got no chance? Whether it's low season or high, it won't stop me winning. I've got this baby sussed."

A verbal spear pierced my back. "That's what you think, boyo. The Easter Bank Holiday's not far away."

Such a friendly chap! Talk about short and sweet – any ideas I might have had of delivering a parting shot were abruptly scuppered by the crashing of his office door.

"Don't worry about old face-ache," a voice piped up behind me. "It's nothing personal. He's the same with everyone."

Concentration now totally decimated and last ball obliterated, I turned to face my mystery ally – a burly fairground worker who beamed me a cynical smile. "Like I said, it's nothing personal. Happens regular as clockwork. He clobbers us all once the tourists arrive. Crafty bugger replaces all the pinball flickers with shorter ones. It's common practice. All the arcade managers do it."

I stared in open-mouthed amazement. "Incredible! You're telling me that they switch the flickers once the season starts? What a load of fiddlers! Do you still play?"

"Nooo ... what's the point when you can't win? All you can do is wait until the season finishes and the holidaymakers go home, because then he changes 'em back again. Like I said, he does it every year. It's just part of the game."

Amazing – with just a few well-chosen words, my fellow pinball connoisseur had managed to sum up a whole new ethos. Nothing like Hendle. Come holiday season, this resort would change markedly: a different town with a different code.

Holidaymakers beware!

⟫ 76 ⟪

The flashing lights and cosmic wolf whistles now seemed a million light-years away as midnight again found me sitting alone in a darkened auditorium. A regular occurrence since my arrival here – not helped by the anguish of delivering another late night double force-feed.

Little wonder that my starry-eyed staff had been so quick to flee the building. After all, who in their right mind would want to be a part of this? Forcibly stuffing two dolphins with fish?

Definitely not them – and certainly not me.

Nevertheless, no matter how bad things seemed, I knew that I couldn't just throw in the towel. I had to remain positive, especially as that quiet voice from within still whispered, *"Life!"*

"Come on, Capello, stop feeling sorry for yourself. You've extra fish thawing in the sink, so get off your backside and give them one last try. After all, what've you got to lose?"

But the splashing of a limp herring in the water yielded little joy other than to bring an excited Scouse racing into the stage.

"When are we gonna start work? I mean, when?"

A clumsy chomp and the fish was gone.

"You comedian, Scouse! That feed wasn't supposed to be for you. It was meant for Duchess or Herb'e."

As customary with this vivacious Atlantean, his ultra-sharp *connection* sliced through my bleary haze like a hot knife through butter.

"Why waste it? They don't want it."

Spot on. Neither one of my *Perfect Pair* had shown the slightest interest in the fish. Even so, Scouse's jubilant mood couldn't help but remind me of the nonchalant attitude my dolphins always adopted when faced with sickness or death – a philosophy that, even after all these years, I found impossible to appreciate.

"You poor fella, Scouse! What with all this rotten trouble, I've seriously neglected you, haven't I? You're itching to perform, and I just don't have the heart for it. So, here and now, my son, I'm gonna make you a promise. Come tomorrow, no matter what happens, you and me are gonna start work. Just like we did in the old days. How does that grab yer?"

Another mouthful of fish stopped any interaction, which just went to show that the one thing capable of shutting up this talkative dolphin was food.

"Okay, people, that's it for tonight. If I don't get some sleep, I'm liable to fall over, so I'll see you tomorrow. As for you, Scouse, it's no good complaining. I've just given you …"

…

… I've just given you …

…

… I've just given you …

…

… a cold shiver ran down my spine.

Someone had just spoken …

… and it wasn't Scouse.

77

Have I just picked up a message, or is my tortured mind playing tricks?

Has that incisive *connection* with Scouse just been compromised?

I can't be sure, but there's suddenly a warm expectancy welling in the pit of my stomach, because I sense that the bond I'm now involved with has a new signature – texture altogether softer, altogether quieter.

Could it be …?

"Duchess, is that you? Did you just say something or what?"

An angry snort shatters the silence.

"Well, come on, girl, don't be shy … Talk to me …"

No answer – yet she *did* speak, I'm certain of it. And, if she did, that means there's been a change – a subtle shift – almost as if one of those barred doors has opened ever so slightly.

I dare not move. Must still my soul and clear my mind – allow her song to filter through.

Waiting … waiting as the minutes turn into an age. But there's nothing – only the echo of the water kissing the foot of the stage.

She's gone. Fallen back into her dream.

Yet I heard her, most definitely heard her.

I feel a smile breaking through.

"Tomorrow, people. See you tomorrow."

Because tomorrow, I have a chance.

78

Early next morning, I found myself standing apprehensively on a deserted stage. Beams of light heralded the birth of a new day, probing the arena's protective veil with muted laser fingers. My alien mirror flickered with infant ballerinas that danced softly across its surface before sparking the sleek contours of my sleeping Atlanteans. As always, the first to steal my gaze was Duchess, half-slumbering and gently weaving the water's wave.

"Hello, beautiful, are we eating today?"

The salt air galvanized my senses as I listened for her song, and, although I perceived no reply, I caught the ending of her dream.

I knew that these first few minutes would be all-important if I were to have any chance of winning her back. There would be no room for hesitation. Somehow, I had to knit a sleepy *connection* into the fabric of her dreamscape – an understated wave to disrupt the rhythm of the mind-set.

I instinctively embraced what appeared to be the beginnings of a dull headache, before closing my eyes to search for that sweet-smelling nausea. Almost immediately, my senses succumbed to a musk perfume – a potent mist that bore an all too familiar scent.

"Hello, girl, I've really missed you."

Although Duchess continued to remain just out of reach, there was no mistaking the mirror's magic in her eyes.

"See, beautiful, I haven't gone anywhere. I've been waiting for you all this time. So the question is, where have you been?"

Ignoring the dank chill of the stage tiles, I dropped belly-down to lie with my arms outstretched.

"Why don't you come closer, Duch? It's been a long while since we had a cuddle."

Flashing the face of my ring, I attempted to catch the soft sunbeams spilling through the dolphinarium skylights.

"You've always loved my ring, haven't you, Duch?"

Tentatively, she inched closer to nose my hand, obviously more interested in the band's lustre than the chunk of herring concealed within my palm. Rolling just beneath the waterline, her huge eyes spirited me soft looks.

"That's more like it. This is just like old times, Duch … you and me, together."

A feeling of pure love drew a rare smile.

"So who's still the most beautiful girl in the world, then? And, more importantly, when is she going to eat?"

Ever so slowly, ever so gently, she opened my hand, taking the fish between her teeth.

I stiffened with expectation …

Eat it, Duch – please, please eat it!

"Come on, girl, don't mess about with that herring – swallow it!"

Drifting lazily, she gave the slightest shake of her head – and the fish was gone.

Thank God!

A soft whistle and a prolonged hug greeted her feed.

"Good girl! Now that wasn't so bad, was it? Do you want another?"

Rolling onto her side, she exposed a white underbelly, blushed with pink.

"Yes …"

Yes, she'd said yes – the first clear word she'd beamed since the trauma at Hendle. As the warmth of her answer washed over me, the penetrating cold of the damp tiles blissfully evaporated.

"Did you just say yes, beautiful? Well, what my girl wants, my girl gets."

"Hey! Hold on! Hold on! What about me? You haven't said hello to me yet!"

Oh no, Scouse! There was no mistaking his rampaging *connection*; yet for one heart-stopping moment, I'd dared to hope, dared to pray, that it might be *him* – my lost Atlantean, Herb'e.

"Come on, Dave, you said we were gonna work today. You promised … You know you did."

Scouse's psychic blast was impossible to hold back. Now fully awake, he had steamrolled himself firmly into the mix.

"Scouse, you're like a bull in a china shop. You're supposed to be asleep. Can't you see that I need a little quality time with my girl?"

Years of experience had taught me that it was pointless arguing with this little dolphin, as there could only ever be one winner. However, my prizefighter's exuberant intrusion had miraculously thrown up an unexpected bonus: from the periphery of my vision, I noticed that Herb'e had abruptly stopped his monotonous circling and was instead drifting ever closer to the stage …

… closer and closer.

❧ 79 ❧

Despite all my efforts to push him out, Scouse continued to wriggle boisterously in front of the stage.

"Not now, Scouse, for goodness' sake, not now!"

As much as I loved my little prizefighter's enthusiasm, the last thing I needed was him hogging the limelight. This was the closest I'd been to Herb'e since our arrival at West Coast, so I couldn't afford any distractions.

"You said we were gonna start work today, no matter what happened. You promised."

The next few minutes were critical: Herb'e was wavering, which meant I only had a short window in time to tempt him back.

"Scouse, please ... not now! I need to talk to Herb'e."

"But you promised, you promised ..."

My raucous Atlantean was now a serious threat to my engaging my sick dolphin, who was a hair's breadth from being driven from the stage.

"Come on, Duchess, I need some help here. I've got to have a clear playing field if I'm gonna reach Herb'e."

I was well aware that, no matter how desperate I might be to make contact, I had to curtail my enthusiasm. Any communication had to be initiated by Herb'e, and Herb'e alone, so I had to play it cool.

Responding to my plea, Duchess immediately swam into action, clearing a passage by pushing and prodding Scouse away from the stage.

"It's not fair. I want to stay ... He promised! He promised!"

Thankfully, my princess was in no mood to negotiate, and – despite all his remonstrations – my dejected little dolphin was escorted back to his corner.

"But you heard him … He promised! He promised!"

Thank goodness – my living barrier now removed, I at last had a clear shot at Herb'e.

"Hello, my son? How are yer feeling?"

I was convinced that Herb'e had opened a channel, though his signal was so weak I could barely feel him.

Moving closer, he tentatively nudged the palm of my hand, which, as always, hid a piece of fish.

"I'd be quick to eat this if I were you, Herb'e, because if you don't, Scouse will nick it."

Forcing his beak deeper into my grasp, I felt the prize slip from my hand.

"There you go, Herb'e! Now that wasn't so bad, was it? I bet you and Duch are feeling pretty hungry about now, so how about I get you some more?"

Although Herb'e remained cocooned within his silent *connection*, both he and Duchess went on to take three pounds of best herring – hardly a feast, but most definitely a start and a heart-lifting trend that continued throughout the rest of the day, eventually culminating in the grand total of twelve pounds of fish each. A lifesaver!

This meant that my dream team had actually consumed more food in one day than they had in well over a week – a sign that the destructive mind-set might well be broken and the horrible force-feeds over.

Just how I'd managed to drag them back from the brink, I didn't know, but I strongly suspected that the shock and distress of being forcibly stuffed with fish had played a huge part. Even so, I couldn't rest on my laurels – I had to push for further feeds as my *Perfect Pair* needed building up fast. This meant I'd be heading for yet another sleepless night. Why? Because the next early-morning feeds would hopefully confirm that our nightmare was over.

"Sorry about the workout, Scouse. We'll definitely go for it tomorrow … I promise!"

❧ 80 ❧

A hint of dawn again spotted me standing on any empty stage, breathless with anticipation.

"Hello, people, are we awake yet?"

As customary, the first to break slumber and switch on his dolphin radio was my ever-reliable Scouse, who immediately bombarded me with excited hellos.

"Are we working today? Are we? Remember, you promised ..."

A pity my *Perfect Pair* didn't share his zest for life – particularly Herb'e, whose once bubbly *connection* remained very tenuous. It was blatantly obvious that in his present state, he would not be ready to perform for some considerable time, no matter how much food he ate.

On top of everything else, I had the feeling that Herb'e was struggling to cope with his new surroundings – something I could fully relate to, because he wasn't the only one floundering in the dark.

Since my arrival at West Coast, I was finding it near impossible to settle. Whether this was down to our horrendous start, I didn't know, but I couldn't shake the persistent feeling of weariness and foreboding generated by this alien pool; confirmation of what I already knew – that all three of us were seriously out of our comfort zone.

On the bright side, although still subdued, Duchess seemed a little more *compos mentis*, meaning I could at least instruct Forrester to hold off with any further force-feeds. However, this didn't mean an end to the vet's visits or Herb'e's gruelling catches – a rigour my sick dolphin could have well done without. Herb'e still required daily medication: injections of multivitamins and antibiotics that would be ongoing for some time. As Forrester had pointed out, Herb'e was one sick dolphin and getting him right was going to be a long haul.

Of paramount concern today was that yesterday's progress in the eating department should continue, as the last thing I needed was Duchess and Herb'e falling back into the starvation mind-set. My *Perfect Pair* were still grossly underweight, and, in their present condition, another venture down the road to force-feeding could well be their last – especially in Herb'e's case.

To make matters worse, the Easter Bank Holidays were only two weeks away, which meant that the Company would soon be demanding shows – performances that Duchess and Herb'e would be unable to fulfil. So, to add to my woes, I now had the unenviable task of informing Clive Rothwell that I'd be opening his precious bank holiday weekend with a one-dolphin show …

… and a blind dolphin at that.

❧ 81 ❧

"David, I know you're going through hell with Duchess and Herb'e, but as West Coast manager I have a duty to keep Head Office abreast of any problems. I'm really sorry, but it's imperative that I know how your team's condition will affect the Easter Bank Holidays."

Clearly, Clive was still patently unaware of just how seriously ill my two stars actually were, which meant I'd have to choose my words carefully.

"Clive, it's only two weeks before the bank holidays kick off and – to be blatantly honest – there's not a chance in hell that Herb'e will be ready. Scouse will have to take over star billing."

His eyes clouded with confusion. "Scouse? Are you sure? I mean, will Scouse be up to partnering Duchess?"

Confusion! Confusion!

"No … you don't understand, Clive. Under no circumstances will I be splitting Duchess and Herb'e. That would be like kicking Herb'e when he's down. He needs Duchess now more than ever, so – for better or for worse – they *have* to stay together." I took a deep breath. "Scouse will be working alone."

The perplexity dulling Clive's eyes now flared into roaring panic.

"Scouse? Working alone? How can he do that? He's blind, for God's sake … He's blind!"

In a show of drama, he slumped across the desk, burying his head in his hands.

"A one-dolphin show!" he wailed. "You're telling me you want to open the Easter Bank Holidays with a blind dolphin in a one-dolphin show? I can't believe it … I just can't believe it's happening again. When you and your team arrived, I thought all our troubles were over … I thought the curse on this pool was lifted … I thought … Oh God! How could I have been so wrong? This is a nightmare!"

Unable to contain his agitation any longer, Clive leapt from his chair. "Head Office … what am I going to tell Head Office? They'll go crazy. The bank holidays are when we make all our money – important revenue to take us through the slow times before we start the season proper. What are they going to say? They'll be expecting shows – shows with two dolphins."

"Well, you can start by telling them the truth," I retorted. "The sad fact is we've only got three dolphins, and two of them are sick – something we can't do anything about. And if they don't like that, then it's just too bad, because I can't work miracles. If they want to make an issue of it, send them to me … Or, better still, send 'em to Forrester."

Hardly words of comfort, graphically illustrated by the pained expression that flashed across his face.

I softened my tone. "Look, Clive, I can't help you with Head Office – they're your problem. But I can help when it comes to Scouse."

"But he's blind! Blind! He can't see! How the heck can he work without another dolphin to guide him?"

"Clive … Clive …" I soothed, "try not to worry. Scouse will be fine. He *can* see – just not in the way we can. Besides, he's all we've got, so you're gonna have to trust me on this one … Okay?"

As he flopped back into his chair, his panic gave way to a final, weary resignation. "Okay, David, whatever you say," he sighed. "You're the trainer, so it's your call. But I still can't believe that this nightmare is happening."

I didn't want to be responsible for driving this mild-mannered man into taking a long walk off a short pier, so I purposely chose not to reveal the true gravity of Duchess and Herb'e's condition. Nevertheless, I was all too aware that my dream team's nightmare was anything but over.

As for Scouse, he had unexpectedly become the new kid on the block, which meant that the enormous pressure of the bank holiday shows would now fall to him.

The clock was ticking, which meant I couldn't delay any longer in testing my little prizefighter. I had to prove that my faith in this blind dolphin was more than just a sentimental whim. It was time to honour my promise to Scouse ...

... the dolphin no one wanted was about to become West Coast's newest star.

⟨ 82 ⟩

"I can't work miracles," I'd said.

Not strictly true – especially when it came to dealing with this sightless Atlantean. Even in my distraught state, I firmly believed that I was the only trainer in the country who had a chance of pulling off these one-dolphin shows. After all, I was the one who'd originally turned Baby and Scouse into top performers – a fact that Management had conveniently chosen to forget.

Restoring Scouse to his former glory without Baby's help was going to be a big ask. Nevertheless, I was convinced I could make it happen. It had always been glaringly obvious that the only way to work Scouse was by thought – the transmission of mind pictures. Even so, what I was about to attempt would be a whole new ball game. It would mean initiating an almost total psychic bond with my little dolphin – quite literally crawling inside him – something I'd achieved in short spells when first training him to beach.

Without doubt, a mind merge with my tiny Titan would be the ultimate test of my thought-based training method – and there *would* be a downside. Bonding for such a long period of time would be mentally exhausting, and I was still very fragile.

The big question now: in my worn-down state, could I mentally hold it together?

I was about to find out.

83

The moment of truth – time to find out just how much my little prizefighter has actually remembered.

The clunk of an overflowing fish bucket brings my exuberant Scouse racing to the stage.

"Are we gonna work? Are yer gonna keep your promise? Are yer? I mean, are yer?"

"Course I am, lad. Just needed a bit more time to get things together, that's all … but I'm here now. Are you excited, 'cause I know I am?"

A shaking head and animated chatter gives me my answer, spurring me to drop to my knees and rough his heavily-lined melon.

"You lovely, lovely man. Now don't get too excited, or you won't be able to concentrate."

Just listen to me. *Scouse* get excited? Who am I trying to kid? He's like a breath of fresh air.

"Ech … ech … ech … ech …" A verbal mishmash that proves he hasn't listened to a word I've just said.

"All right, Scouse – I'm glad to see you too, but we can't mess around because we've got a lot of work to do. I still have to find out if I've got my old boy back."

Multiple squawks of expectation … More frenzied head shaking.

"Now, slow down, Scouse, just cool it. Today we're gonna work on the beaching trick – something we did way back at Hendle. Do you remember?"

Of all the tricks in his lost repertoire, this is the only one that can give me the reassurance I need, because, for this blind dolphin, the beaching is undoubtedly the ultimate test.

"Right, Scouse, we need to work together. I'm gonna close my eyes and try to find you – but you've got to calm down, 'cause we can't do this while you're jumping around."

Whoa!

Bang! I'm in!

It's incredible – not an ounce of hesitation. Literally as quick as throwing a light switch.

"You, my son, are amazing. It's as if we've never been apart."

Head cocked, he opens wide his mouth, flashing me a brown toothy smile and wagging grey tongue. There can be no doubt about it, this raucous little dolphin is most definitely a senior citizen.

"Ohh! That feels good, doesn't it, lad? This connection is really rocking, so let's find that picture, shall we? The one of a boy and a dolphin."

Scouse's head gently sways from side to side, and I feel his psyche roll behind my eyes.

"Found it, Dave … found the picture."

God! I'm glad he has, because I'm still lost in space. Got to apply the brakes and slow him down; Scouse is racing ahead of me in the mind stakes.

"Hold your horses, my son – I'm not there yet."

He's impetuous, trying to rush me into the vision, that's how eager he is to get going. My prizefighter reminds me of a thoroughbred nudging the starting gate, bubbling to explode at the sound of the bell. I've got to hold him back, because I'm still not focussed … still haven't found that all-important picture.

"More time, Scouse. I need more time."

It's amazing … even without my input, he has evolved. His psyche is so sharp that he's actually reversing our roles, meaning *he's* now the lead player.

"Need to trance myself, Scouse – concentrate on that hypnotic patch of water just behind your head."

What's wrong with me? He's ready and I'm not. Come on, Capello, get a move on, because he won't wait forever.

"Found it, Scouse … found the picture!"

Incredible – my senses see his battle-torn body, feel his every imperfection. I can even gauge his weight.

"You've put on a few pounds since we last worked together, haven't you, lad?"

Reflections From

FLIPPA · DUCHESS

The Mirror

Capello performing the double fish hand with Duchess and Herb'e.

Capello and Duchess.
He promised to always stay by her side, swore he'd never leave her.

Warning! Warning! Warning! The dastardly duo – the unconquerable Smelly and Worse!

Capello's Vulcan first officer – the handsome Dan Conner!

"You lovely, lovely lad! Give us a kiss, Herb'e!"

Head nodding, head shaking – Capello and Herb'e deep in psychic conversation.

TAIJI

TAIJI DEATH COVE

WHERE JAPAN DRINKS THE BLOOD OF ATLANTIS

Lest we forget … each year on 1st September, this Japanese mafia town embarks on its horrific 6-month slaughter of Atlanteans, butchering some 2000 in its notorious Killing Cove. In addition, as a lucrative sideline, it supplies the global aqua-circus with the vast majority of its captive entertainers.

Some scientists believe that a dolphin's intelligence rivals that of a 6-7 year-old child (others believe even greater), so wish to see dolphins reclassified as non-human persons.

In any language, the Taiji hunt equates to nothing less than slavery and mass murder the systematic genocide of a sentient culture.

Citizens of Taiji - the custodians of time will forever remember this shame.

"But this water's so filthy, I just assumed you'd be dumping?"
On hearing this, Backhouse visibly stiffened.

The scrubbing out of a shallow, filth-ridden holding pen.

"For eighteen hours, I watched them drift in cramped cesspools whilst Backhouse implemented his ill-planned water bleaching policy ..."

That fateful night: "... a thirteen-foot drop ... a long way down ... a very, very long way down ..."

"What I wouldn't give to experience Herb'e's impish schoolboy sparkle for just one more time …"

"The toothbrush — my mischievous Herb'e's favourite trick!"

*Duchess and Herb'e's magnificent double back somersault –
the first movement in Capello's revered shadow ballet.*

*The animated Capello as he wills Duchess and Herb'e into the second
movement of the shadow ballet – the spectacular body spins!*

The superb Duchess and Herb'e – hurdling in perfect unison!

The bond is plain to see. Capello with the love of his life – Duchess!

Capello's morning task loading the vit-fish.
"… quite literally like giving candy to a baby."

A spectacular moment in time capturing the brilliance of my Perfect Pair.

My beloved rugged little prizefighter performing his opening bows! Sadly, the only photograph to survive the ravages of time.

Early days in the making of The Perfect Pair.
Capello teaches the hurdle to a young Duchess and Herb'e.

Capello and Duchess – inseparable!
"How did something so beautiful turn so ugly?"

"Happy days! Up-close and personal with my mischievous Herb'e."

Capello always believed in close physical contact with his charges.

Bonnie and Clyde's fabulous double beaching – a trick much admired by Capello.

Unknown dolphin beaching at Hendle.
A beautiful photograph of a handsome Atlantean!

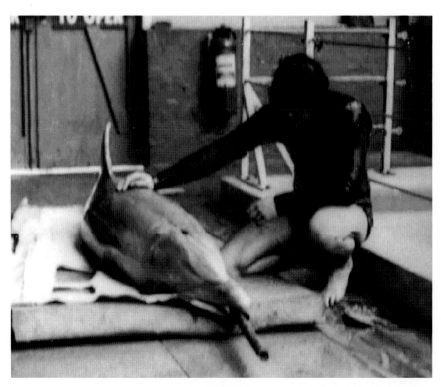

A wet-suited Capello preparing a dolphin for transport.

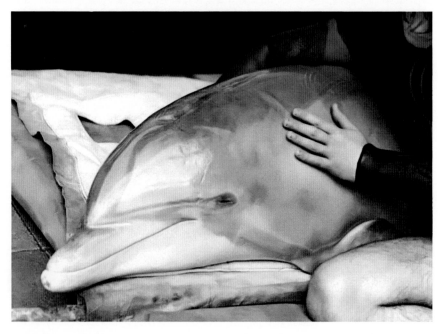

Twinkle succumbing to the psychic whispers of Capello in preparation for transport.

Always a nerve-racking time –
Capello dousing one of his dolphins during a transport.

A common method of transport: dolphin in a canvas sling
suspended in a waterproof plastic "coffin box".

Duchess – eyes fixed firmly on Capello - performs her magnificent tail walk.

A truly dynamic photo of Duchess and Herb'e spearing through the double hoops!

Dan performing the double fish hand.

Duchess and Herb'e performing the double back somersault in perfect unison!

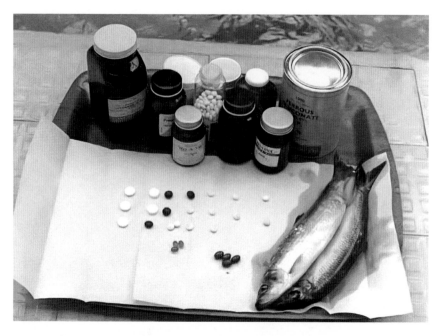

All vitamins counted and checked before the morning administration.

Capello's eyes say it all — that shattered look.
"Dolphinariums don't just break dolphins, they break people too."

Clever boy – he's not answering because he knows I'm still not fully in the mix so doesn't want to break my concentration, which means he's not prepared to let me get away with this warm-up routine for much longer. I can feel the pressure building; yet even this nagging discomfort is laced with exhilaration – something I haven't felt for a long time.

"Right, Scouse, I'm on board ... I can see the boy ... see the dolphin."

A lone Atlantean and a lone human sharing an empty stage.

It's surreal ... Although my eyes stay fixed on the mirror, I feel his every muscle flexing, his every sinew straining ...

"Are you ready, Scouse? Are you ready to go?"

A million stars explode behind my eyes, and *we* bullet from the water onto the cold, hard tiles – two minds fused inside one battered body ...

... a vision replayed.

"Tail up! Come on, Scouse, tail up! We've got to get our tail up ..."

A dull ache tugs at the base of my spine, and *our* heart skips a beat. Then comes the heave – that monumental heave.

"We're not there yet, Scouse! The trick isn't complete until our tail's held high."

I feel the strain ... the pain ... the excitement... the expectation.

❧ 84 ❧

On stage, I see a boy kneeling on his left leg, right arm locked straight as a gun barrel and rigidly pointing at something hidden within the mirror's plane. His entire form is motionless, and his face is etched with strain. I note how his left arm is unnaturally extended behind his crouched body, as if dislocated – a surreal pose that leaves the palm of his hand flattened skywards. His concentration is such that I can't be sure he's even breathing – flesh and bone turned to stone by a Gorgon's gaze.

Nonetheless, from this vantage point, I can see that he's not alone. Hiding in his shadow is the arc of a dolphin with tail held high. Two statues allied by an insurmountable bond of love … or could it be infatuation?

This is a vision I've seen before: a boy and an Atlantean in classic pose – something I never tire of seeing, yet still find impossible to rationalize. After all, how can a person *be* in two places at the same time?

My inherent ability to detach my psyche from my physical form never fails to get me rattled. And it's happening more and more – a phenomenon that some would like to attribute to neurosis.

But they'd be wrong … so very wrong!

"Great, Scouse! Absolutely fantastic! You clever, clever lad. I knew you could do it … I knew you hadn't forgotten … I just knew!"

❧ 85 ❧

A glorious five seconds later and a long shriek of the whistle signalled an end to the test.

"Okay, Scouse, now try to relax while I get you back into the water."

I never ceased to be amazed at the speed with which my metal mouthpiece could end a *connection* – unconditional trust totally decimated by something as simple as the sound of a whistle.

"Calm down, Scouse! You know I'll get you back in one piece…"

I was painfully aware that I should have tried to hold him on stage for a while longer, but the strain would have been too great. The blast of the whistle wasn't only a release for Scouse, it was a release for me as well.

Taking a deep breath, I slid my left forearm beneath his chin and my right hand beneath his chest before giving one almighty heave.

"There you go, Scouse … back where you belong. Now for your reward – a well-deserved fish bonanza."

I couldn't help smiling as I watched the herring feast slide down his gullet.

"You're like a wide-mouthed frog, Scouse, you really are! Anyway, I've got some good news. You've passed your test with flying colours, which means you're going to get your day in the sun. You, my friend, are going to be the star of the bank holiday shows."

He understood that all right – my little fella was ecstatic.

"Hey, that was great – really, really great! Where did he learn to do that?"

A voice from the shadows – it seemed that our beaching session hadn't been as private as I'd first thought. Scouse and I had attracted a hidden admirer – a young presenter.

Turning, I smiled. "Hendle, that's where. I taught him to beach at Hendle when he was part of the Baby and Scouse team. I can't understand why no one here knew about it … After all, his beaching is in his logbooks for all to see."

I had never once doubted that this little dolphin was special – something I hoped would become apparent to an unappreciative Management. It was just a shame that the recognition he so richly deserved would be founded on the failing reputations of those I treasured most: Duchess and Herb'e …

… my not so *Perfect Pair*.

86

My two favourite people have now fully emerged from their mystic hideaway. However, I'm all too aware that I'll have to monitor them constantly, as any sudden drop in their food intake might easily catapult them back into the nightmare realm of force-feeding.

The dolphin mind-set is a dangerous dreamscape, and its allure will always pose a threat. I've witnessed its power on too many occasions – particularly in the training pens of North Liston – and know all too well that once the doors to this twilight realm have opened, they are near impossible to close.

This portal seems to emit a siren rhythm, one that has already enticed Duchess and Herb'e on two separate occasions. It is a deadly invitation, because, with every fleeting visit, the astral thief hiding within spirits away willpower … little by little … bit by bit … until …

No. This isn't over – not by a long chalk.

Even so, today of all days, I don't intend to waste my reprieve by harbouring dark thoughts, because I've too much to be thankful for. First, I've put Clive Rothwell right. Second, I've proven that my little prizefighter is in rude health. Third – and most importantly – I've managed to claw back Herb'e.

Time to celebrate, starting with an overdue visit to the amusement arcade to liaise with my *Killer Babe from Outer Space* … whilst at the same time hopefully irritating her po-faced pimp.

Great!

If I'm slick, I'll 'ave just enough time to squeeze in a couple of games and heap even more misery on old face-ache.

Strange … today the arcade is busier than usual, but I don't see any of the regular players. Wonder where they've got to? Still, no time to worry about them – I've got to claim my machine before someone else does.

I'm in luck – nobody's stolen her away, which means I can give my favourite alien another intergalactic kicking.

Not much money – or time, for that matter – so I'll have to get my skates on … go straight into kick-ass mode. God, I love roughing up this pinball machine … especially when old misery guts is watching.

…

Wha …! Wha …!

You must be kidding! It's tilted … the bloody thing's tilted, and I hardly even touched it. Now I'm behind, which means I can't afford any more slip-ups … need to go softly-softly with this second ball …

…

No! No! No! No!

I don't believe it! I don't flippin' believe it! *How* the hell did that ball get through? I had the thing covered … I'm sure I had it covered! My God, Capello, come on, get a grip! A rank amateur could've hit that one, and you're two balls down now.

Bloody thing … bloody, rotten thing!

Right, darlin', this is it … Final ball … Payback time! This is when I take you apart …

...

Shit!

I missed it! Missed the soddin' thing! How the hell did that happen? I mean, how?

Shit!

Shit! Shit! Shit! Shit! Shit!

I've lost ... I've *actually* lost ... the rotten, thieving thing!

...

Right! *Right!*

Right, Capello, don't dwell! Just get yourself together. You can't let this robbin' contraption beat yer a second time.

Talk about Custer's last stand! Still, can't make a song and dance about losing – especially not with old misery guts clockin' me.

"What's wrong, boyo, lost your touch?"

Boyo? Did he say boyo? I hate it when he calls me that ... really, *really* hate it ... and, what's more, he knows it.

Keep shtum, Capello ... Don't give him the satisfaction of an answer. Just concentrate on your game.

He's smirkin' at me ... actually smirkin' ... the cocky sod! Trying to wind me up ... trying to put me off! Well, it's not gonna work ... I'm gonna wipe that smirk right off his ugly, fat face!

...

He's *still* smirkin' ... like he *knows* I'm gonna lose ...

...

And now I know why ...

He's done it!

The rotten fiddler's actually gone and done it!

He's altered the tilt mechanism and replaced the flickers.

The crafty bugger! No wonder all the regulars have gone AWOL. Him changing those flickers can mean only one thing – the bank holiday build-up has started, meaning no more pinball for me. It's tourists only from now on ... and shows ...

... non-stop shows.

❦ 88 ❧

The next two days saw Duchess and Herb'e consuming only three pounds of fish between them – confirmation that their feeds had again crashed and the nightmarish dolphin mind-set returned. Utterly catastrophic, as in their weakened condition, this would undoubtedly send them hurtling back into their mystic hideaway. I felt like screaming, as I knew that another visit to this shadowy realm could well be their last.

I was convinced that the horror of the recent force-feeds had shocked my team back from the brink, just as it had in those early days at North Liston. However, the continuing trauma of veterinary treatment had pushed Herb'e over the edge, leaving him suicidal – a state of mind that would not only propel *him* to his doom, but Duchess as well. Herb'e's shattered psyche was now openly embracing the endgame, which meant I had no choice but to adopt a desperate measure – a shake session.

"Listen, you two. I'm not going to stand idly by and let you drift nonchalantly into the labyrinth of the mind-set ... I won't!"

This was, without doubt, a flawed decision, but Duchess and Herb'e weren't the only ones now dancing on the edge of chaos – the constant worry and weeks of sleep deprivation had finally driven me to utter despair.

I was breaking, and an abyss was beckoning ...

... beckoning and threatening to consume us all.

It didn't work … the shake session didn't work … didn't bring Duchess and Herb'e back. All it did was drive them even deeper into the mind-set, and – no matter how I try – I can't seem to pull them out.

Even Forrester believes that there's no way back, telling me that I should prepare myself for the worst. No wonder, because he's saying it's been a full ten days – ten horrendous days and nights of exhausting catches and force-feeds. Not that I'd know, because I'm so disorientated that time no longer has any meaning.

Is it day? Or is it night?

I'm not sure, anymore, because under these artificial lights, day and night are irrelevant – everything blurs into one.

With each catch, each force-feed, my bruised and battered body screams ever louder – but my mind remains strangely detached. It's as if I've become an automaton … a soulless automaton …

A soulless automaton – Affirmative.

A soulless automaton – Activate.

Catch and detain Duchess – Affirmative.

Input fish – Affirmative.

Monitor food intake. Imperative to avoid regurgitation – Affirmative.

Release Duchess – Affirmative.

Catch and detain Herb'e – Affirmative.

Input fish – Affirmative.

Monitor food intake. Imperative to avoid regurgitation – Affirmative.

Release Herb'e – Affirmative.

It's horrible – Affirmative.

It's soul-destroying – Affirmative.

Affirmative … Affirmative … Affirmative …

I'm tormented … sick with worry … don't know how much more I can take.

I can't eat … can't swallow … the very sight of food closes my throat.

Cigarettes … I'm living on cigarettes … and tea …

What am I gonna do? What am I gonna do?

My two dolphins are literally fading away before my eyes, and I'm powerless to do anything about it. But I can't give up … can't write them off, whatever Forrester says. He doesn't know them like I do … He doesn't understand the mechanics of the dolphin psyche. In fact, why the hell am I even listening to him? He's just a vet, for God's sake … just another overpaid scientist.

I've got to stay positive – keep the faith – especially in Duchess' case, because, deep down, I know she's still out there, comforting Herb'e. In fact, I'm certain of it, because I can still feel her *connection* – that psychic bond – and while I have that, I have her … and, maybe, Herb'e too.

Ten days … ten days … I still can't believe that it's been ten days since that ill-conceived shake session.

What was I thinking? How can I ever forgive myself for what I did? What I said? Beating the water like a maniac and screaming:

"I've 'ad enough … I can't take this anymore! This isn't a holiday camp. You two are here to work … work till you drop … so the sooner you get used to it, the better, because the only way either of you is ever getting out of here is in a box. Do yer copy? Are yer listening to me …? Well, are yer …?"

Madness … utter madness. I totally lost it … totally snapped, chastising, in the cruellest way, the two most special people in my life.

And for what?

Even if Duchess and Herb'e do recover, they're going absolutely nowhere. It's like I said, the only way they will ever escape this horrible existence is tail-first …, which makes *me* … what …?

A glorified gaoler … working on death row.

God, dolphinariums! Bloody dolphinariums! How I …

"David, are you finished with the force-feeds? We've got a big queue waiting outside, and we can't afford to run behind schedule."

The usherette – the echo of her voice booming from the top of the auditorium.

Big queue waiting outside … Running behind schedule … It can't be … Surely it can't be …

But it is. It's here. It's actually here. The bank holiday weekend. Once again, I've lost time – nearly two weeks of my life.

"David, I'm sorry to push you, but I need to know when I can let them in."

She's right – we can't keep the public waiting any longer. No matter how bad things are, there's money to be made, and the Company will always demand its pound of flesh. So this is it.

"Yeah, I'm finished with Duchess and Herb'e for now, so you may as well let them in."

I'm so shattered that I can barely drag myself into the shower, let alone do a show. Hardly the best way to go into the most demanding weekend of my life, but, ready or not, the onslaught is about to start.

"Come on, Scouse, let's get ready to rumble, because it's just you and me, now, kid … just you and me."

❦ 90 ❧

As I slouch in the wings of the stage, I'm overwhelmed by a sudden desire to throw up – no doubt a symptom of weeks without sleep.

It's strange, but even in my exhausted state, my ears are able to gauge the size of the audience – a reminder that, as long as my other senses remain keen, I can do without my eyes. An ability my little prizefighter has long since mastered.

God, what a challenge we face today. For him, as a show dolphin, the biggest day of his life – the day he *hopefully* proves all his doubters wrong. For me, as his trainer, the biggest day of my life – the day I *hopefully* prove the validity of my thought-based training method.

Yeah ... it doesn't come any bigger than this!

Scouse ... Wonder what he's thinking, alone in that pool with all those expectant faces looking on? A multitude breathlessly waiting just for *him*. What a blast! What a thrill!

Strange, I'm still nauseous, but that weary, sinking feeling seems to be dissipating, which means that my adrenaline pump is kicking in.

"What a show we're gonna give 'em, Scouse! What a show!"

He's listening ... I *know* that he's listening ... hearing what I'm hearing ... latching on to the turbulent crowd's noisy excitement. Kids whinging at dad because they want a better seat, want to get closer to the action. Kids whining at mum because their sticky, candy-flossed fingers feel grubby.

The trials of family life! Makes me wonder just who's in the best place right now – those moth-eaten parents or me? A no-brainer really ... As bad as things are, it has to be me, most definitely me.

174

Above the mayhem, I can hear the auditorium doors banging shut, a sure sign that it won't be long before I'm on stage and facing my greatest challenge. There's also that scent of gardenia radiating from the pretty compère who's standing perilously close behind me. I can only pray that she's as good on that mic as she looks in that micro mini-skirt – just in case.

"Right, gorgeous, on you go – and give 'em rice!"

Wow! What a smile – what a beautiful smile! I never noticed before just how lovely she is. But now's not the time. Come on, Capello, forget about her – you've got enough on your plate.

"Ladies and gentlemen, boys and girls, put your hands together and give a warm welcome to your trainer … Mr David Capello!"

Finally – show time.

"Come on, my son, let's 'ave em!"

❧ 91 ❧

Walking on stage to embrace my plaudits, I suddenly spy him hiding in the packed auditorium – about eight rows back and to my right, surrounded by dozens of animated faces: Clive Rothwell, trying unsuccessfully to be invisible. Poor bloke – he looks utterly mortified, as if he can hardly bear the strain.

Not surprising, really, after all, he has a lot to lose – but, then again, haven't we all? Either way, he's not my problem right now. I've got a show to do. What's important is that I concentrate only on Scouse – cement that all-important *connection*.

"Hello, my son, this is the big day. Are you ready for this?"

Why am I even bothering to ask? The mirror is sparking energy – he's ready all right!

Whatever I do, I've got to hold back … daren't walk to the front of the stage too soon. I need to visualise him, drink him in. It's imperative that our first encounter be of the mind, so I need time to focus my third eye – sketch an image of him bobbing in the water, waving that battered head from side to side. Only then will I be able to feed on his enthusiasm.

"Come on, Dave, why are you hanging back there? What are we waiting for? Let's get going!"

Wow! We're connected – no doubt about it – because that message came through loud and clear. It's time to get this show on the road.

Talk about the spirit willing, but the body weak, I can't even feel the three steps I'm taking towards the front of the stage, or the flex of my muscles as I throw back my arm. The only thing I'm picking up is the picture now crystalizing behind my eyes: a portrait – again viewed from afar – of a boy standing pensively on a stage, a mask of concentration blanketing his face.

I am witnessing the re-birth of the puppetmaster, only this time, I'm not sure who is actually pulling the strings – me or Scouse.

Then, it hits me – the breathless exhilaration of cold water smashing into my senses, a pummelling tsunami that rips away the cobwebs of my fatigued mind.

"Oh, fantastic, Scouse! What a rush! I feel like I'm on a rollercoaster."

My entire body is tingling as his electrifying enthusiasm steals my psyche. I can only describe what I'm experiencing as akin to being thrust into a room filled with laughter – mayhem, total and utter joyous mayhem. We are two beings held as one, trapped in a bubble of raucous abandon.

"Are you okay, David? I'm not going too fast, am I?"

Fast? I don't know where I'm up to. Scouse has totally taken me over – even more so than during our recent beaching session. This isn't my bond; it's his. I am listening to a language of pure emotion, yet I understand every word, every single word.

The rush of water swirling around my body and crashing into my ears is so turbulent that I can barely hear the compère or the shriek of the whistle. But weirder, much weirder, is my viewpoint – it's changed.

I now appear to be looking up at someone who looks remarkably like me.

"Take no notice of him, Dave … We've got this in hand – you and me together."

I don't know how, but I know that Scouse is right – dead right. We don't need that bloke with the long hair and the whistle – don't need him at all. We've got this show covered – me and Scouse … Or I *should* say, Scouse and me.

"Heck, Scouse, I don't know where I'm up to. All I know is that I'm shattered … totally shattered!"

"Don't worry about it, Dave, you'll get used to it. Just go with the flow."

Go with the *what*? He's got to be kidding. I'm in a daze, and my mind is quite literally flea jumping, like flicking through the pages of a comic book – framed pictures all taken from different perspectives.

Left side elevation – boy and a dolphin.

Right side elevation – boy and a dolphin.

Top elevation – boy and a dolphin.

And now, this new viewpoint I'm experiencing – looking up from the waterline at … at …

This is getting seriously eerie, because looking at that doppelgänger on stage is really freaking me out. I mean, do I really look like that?

"Hang in there, Dave, we're nearly there … just the final bows, then it's over."

What's he talking about – over?

"The show, silly! The closing bows end the show!"

There I go again, forgetting that the *connection* works both ways.

A sudden thunderclap in my ears and the scream of a high-pitched whistle abruptly snap me back, then … then … I hear a faraway voice.

"Fantastic show, ladies and gentlemen – a truly fantastic show. So put your hands together for the fabulous Scouse and his trainer, David Capello."

Faces … lots and lots of smiling faces. I'm back on stage, and the performance has finished. To my right is the pretty compère, and before me I see an exultant Clive Rothwell galloping down the steps of the auditorium. Then, last but not least, I look down to see the scarred face of my little prizefighter.

Scouse – my magical, incredible, beautiful Scouse …

… my hero!

❦ 92 ❧

"I wouldn't have believed it if I hadn't seen it with my own eyes! I mean, Scouse, for God's sake, working alone without a guide. It's amazing."

I afforded myself a secret smile. Clive's enthusiastic appraisal was certainly in marked contrast to the bout of amateur dramatics he'd treated me to during our previous meeting.

"How do you think he'll stand up to the rest of the bank holiday weekend, because we're going to need five or six shows a day?"

Good question. Although we'd successfully navigated through one show, a further three days of these rigours would be an altogether different matter.

"It's in the lap of the gods, Clive. These show schedules would be a punishing ask for two dolphins, let alone one. But, if it's any consolation, if I had to put my money on anyone, it'd be Scouse, because, without doubt, he's one tough little number."

Not surprisingly, Clive had neglected to ask just how the other half of the act would fare – namely me. The euphoria generated by this first show would be hard, if not impossible, to maintain, especially with the two daily force-feeds I had to contend with. It was going to be arduous, to say the least, but I'd always known that this Easter Bank Holiday would take no prisoners, so it was pointless moaning. I'd just have to get on with it.

"David, we have to open the doors. By the size of the crowd, it looks like it's going to be a full house."

God, here we go again – round two. Now where's that delicious little compère in the short skirt?

93

"Unfortunately, folks, Europe's finest are laid up with a mystery bug, so won't be performing any shows today. But try not to worry … I'm sure it won't be long before Duchess and Flippa are back to their old selves, wowing audiences. So rather than disappoint you all, it's our pleasure to introduce you to a new kid on the block … the latest star of the West Coast Dolphinarium … Scouse!"

Wow – impressive! This compère has certainly got to grips with the opening spiel. She sounds so convincing that even *I* believe her.

"So ladies and gentlemen, boys and girls, I give you the Donny Osmond of the dolphin world – Scouse's trainer … David Capello!"

Now she's *really* getting cocky! Donny Osmond of the dolphin world? Where the heck did that come from? Whatever, her witty quip has certainly worked the oracle – the punters are actually drumming their feet. Just the kick-start I need.

"Right, Dave, get yourself together, because we haven't got all day."

Amazing, Scouse is still bubbling from the last show – he can't wait to get going. I only wish I felt the same way.

"Well, I'm glad you're keen, lad, because I feel shattered."

An understatement: Scouse's adrenaline-fuelled takeover of the previous performance has already drained away – and what's more, he knows it. He's taking no chances, upping his psychic bombardment to keep me on the ball, a mental assault that's left me dithering on the stage in helpless confusion. Something my astute compère has already clocked – it seems I've missed my first cue.

"Come on, Dave, let's get this show on the road."

Scouse, again, head cocked and swaying from side to side, dissecting the air for sound ... or is it light? I'm never quite sure. Either way, he's doing some serious fine-tuning, seeking to pinpoint the right frequency – my frequency. Only problem is, I'm so exhausted that I can't give him any help. My head is literally all over the place – I'm too tired to even move my legs.

"Sorry for the delay, folks, but our trainer's obviously having a serious heart-to-heart with his dolphin before we start – he wants to make sure we get a good show."

The compère's covering ... launching into ad-lib mode ... knows I'm wobbling. I hear the panic in her voice, but I can't respond. Head feels mushy ... spinning ... spinning ... like I'm about to pass out ...

"Come on, Scouse ... I'm desperate ... I need a lift ..."

"Ha! There you are, Dave ... thought for a minute I'd lost you. Are you okay?"

Thank God! This dolphin is truly incredible – he's just flicked the switch, mentally dragging me back into the game. Suddenly, everything's crystal clear, all confusion gone.

"Yeah, I'm ready, Scouse – as ready as I'll ever be."

Have to take a deep breath ...

"Right, lad, now ... hold ... hold ... go!"

Scouse is in the air, performing his opening bows, and I've barely had time to give the signal. His sheer enthusiasm has catapulted him to abnormally impressive heights, not only blowing away the audience, but me too ... I feel reborn!

The shriek of my whistle brings my ecstatic prizefighter racing back to the stage, a wall of thunderous applause at his back.

"Was that good or what, Dave? Did you like that? Well, did you?"

Now *he's* getting cocky!

"Yeah, that was great, but we've got a long way to go, so don't overdo it, Scouse... Now, remind me, which trick comes next?"

I'm ruefully aware that the whistle stimulus is more for my sake than for his, because Scouse doesn't need it. He's again in the driving seat, and I am but a passenger, left breathless with the sheer enthusiasm of his song. He's hurtling from trick to trick at super speed, making it almost impossible for me to keep up with him.

What a super dolphin! What a truly super dolphin!

"Remember, Scouse, don't overdo it. If you carry on at this rate, you'll burn yourself out – and me with yer!"

I barely hear the final blast of the whistle over the deafening applause.

"What an absolutely fantastic show, folks. Incredible – a star is born!"

She's right there – but, then again, *I* never doubted him for second.

"Ladies and gentlemen, boys and girls, let's all put our hands together for the magnificent Scouse and his trainer … David Capello!"

We've done it. Yet, how can I claim any of the credit? I started today in cloud-cuckoo land, and Scouse carried the performance with no help from me … and without another dolphin to lead him. He's just proven comprehensively that he doesn't need his eyes; only his consciousness – and someone who cares sufficiently to access it.

Crowd finally departed, I rough his head – only to spot Clive Rothwell furtively watching from the back of the auditorium, obviously there to seek confirmation that the first show wasn't just a fluke.

"Another great show, David. Fantastic! I still can't believe what I'm seeing."

No, I bet he can't – or anyone else for that matter.

Oh ye of little faith!

Grinning, I turn to Scouse.

"Well, lad, two shows down, two more to go. So what do you think? Are you up for it?"

With a thrilled shake of his head, he answers loud and clear:

"Yeah – when do we go again?"

It's a big ask, but maybe – just maybe – we'll actually get through today's shows in one piece.

"That's the spirit, Scouse! Now, remember, just don't *overdo it!"*

❧ 94 ❧

Three spectacular days whizzed past, and the dolphinarium throbbed with excitement. Scouse – the dolphin no one wanted – was now the saviour of the Easter Bank Holidays. More importantly, his shows were all performed to virtually full houses – financially, a record-breaking bonus that sent Clive Rothwell and the West Coast Management into raptures.

Without doubt, the last seventy-two hours had seen my little prizefighter's inner light shine twice as bright. A welcome uplift for everyone involved in the shows – none more so than me, because his sheer enthusiasm had acted like a super powered battery charger, revitalising my exhausted psyche. Even though I was still administering Duchess and Herb'e's punishing force-feeds, Scouse had blessed me with new hope.

Slouching across the seats of a deserted auditorium, I watched proudly as both staff and Management paid homage to their new star – a rare opportunity for this luckless Atlantean to wallow in a glory I feared he might never experience again …

… for it was man's curse to forget – especially when man wore a suit.

An added bonus to Scouse's success was a bout of unexpected good weather, one that left the West Coast resort simmering in a soft April heat wave. By early afternoon, the dolphinarium was bathed in sunlight. Again, the pool's face birthed heat faeries, light beings that surfed across its face – a dazzling reminder of the enchanted mirror I'd left so far behind.

"Well, Scouse, it's the final day and we've got a heavy schedule ahead of us. The first show is less than an hour away, so you and me need to get ourselves ready."

Scouse's loud guttural squawk and wagging head gave me the answer I'd hoped for, and by twelve-thirty, we were again performing to a packed audience.

My ever-reliable Atlantean continued from where he'd left off the previous day – at the top of his game. However, by the third show, his enthusiasm had visibly waned, and it was clear that the rigours of the last three days were finally taking their toll. Come the penultimate show, the final blow of the whistle came as a welcome relief to us both.

"Poor fella, I know you're shattered, but I've got to ask you for one last show. Do you think you can handle it?"

No answer – my weary dolphin floated sideways at the foot of the stage, the normally buzzy static from his dolphin radio uncharacteristically absent.

"Aww … come on, Scouse … just one more. Gimme just one more show, then we're done. I promise."

My plea was falling on deaf ears. My little dolphin had totally shut himself down.

"God, it's all right for some, Scouse. I wish I could just turn off like you, because, right now, I feel like I'm about to keel over."

Scouse drifted belly-up at the stage edge, wrapped in silence, meaning that my blackmailing tactic had failed miserably. Still, it was worth one more try:

"Come on, Scouse, don't let me down now. Please, just one more show … that's all I ask …"

It was then that I experienced it – the re-opening of a channel …

At first, I automatically thought that Scouse had answered my request. However, I quickly realised that this link was markedly different from that of my blind dolphin: this *connection* rolled softly behind my eyes like a tranquil wave, which could mean only one thing …

… Duchess.

⪻ 95 ⪼

Duchess, my beautiful, beautiful Duchess …

I advanced hesitantly, almost too afraid to look and suddenly overwhelmed by a numbing self-doubt as to my ability to differentiate between the individual songs of my dolphins.

"Please, let it be you, Duchess … Please, let it be you …"

Craning my neck, I half peeped into the sunken belly of the holding pen, then took a deep breath.

"Hello, my lovely, is that you? Where have you been? I've missed you."

All my pent-up agitation immediately dissolved as I met her hypnotic blue eyes and realised that that faraway look was gone.

"I've been away … been with Herb'e … But I'm back now."

A soft smile masked my relief.

"You've been gone an awful long time, girl … fourteen days, to be precise. And how about Herb'e? Has he come back too? I have to ask, because I still can't find him."

I stiffened as a wave of hesitancy washed through our bond.

"I'm not sure … Herb'e's changed … changed a lot. Part of him wants to return … but part of him wants to move on."

Not hard to believe – Herb'e's song was now so weak that it survived only in my memory. Even so, I sensed something: a presence hidden in the void – one I'd all but forgotten.

"So is Herb'e with you or not?"

"Like I said, David, Herb'e's changed … just as you have changed."

There was no fooling my princess. To her, my psyche was an open book. She was telling me what I already knew – that Herb'e wasn't the only one who'd lost himself on that fateful Hendle transport. I too had lost my way.

The never-ending pressure of the last few months had resurrected that latent fury conceived in the torment of the Backhouse grind – a state of mind that demanded rather than asked. Duchess was right: I had changed, and not for the better.

Nevertheless, her unexpected re-emergence from the dolphin mind-set had given me a chance to redeem myself, because, with her returned, I knew that Herb'e would not be far away, lingering on the fringes of the maze.

If I wished to retrieve him, I'd have to act fast.

However, as always, there was a problem: both Duchess and Herb'e were in a fragile state and unfit to perform. Yet allowing them a period of recuperation as I'd done before had proven – in hindsight – to be a great mistake, which meant I needed to think outside the box.

My dream team had been born in the hurly-burly of shows – a baptism that had quickly elevated them to supreme performers. An eminence now lost to the unlikeliest of rivals – the blind colleague who shared their home. For Duchess, this demotion to second billing would be intolerable, because she had grown used to being the centre of attention.

Not for the first time, I found myself breaking into a smile. Even when trapped within the maze of death, my indomitable diva could not resist returning to claim her throne. In other words, Scouse's unbreakable spirit had again weaved its magic – the audience clamour for his shows had been the catalyst to lead Duchess home. As for Herb'e, only time would tell. But I couldn't delay any longer – previous experience had taught me *not* to look a gift horse in the mouth – so, there and then, I decided to put my *Perfect Pair* back to work, a decision that would seem nothing short of lunacy to most people. But, then again, *I* wasn't most people.

"Look, while you two have been away on your travels, worrying me to death, poor old Scouse has been doing all the work. Just look at him – the little fella's so shattered, he can hardly move. So how about you give him a break and do this last show? What do you think?"

Duchess' blowhole closed abruptly as she caught her breath.

"Don't worry, Duch," I added encouragingly, *"it's no big deal. I'll drop all the major jump tricks and somersaults, so you won't get tired. It's about time we got*

back to work, and there's nothing like a show to blast away those cobwebs. I mean, what have you got to lose?"

It was obvious that she still wasn't convinced, meaning this would take all my powers of persuasion.

"Look, give it a shot. It's the least you can do. After all, what's one more show?"

What's one more show?

EVERYTHING!

With trepidation, I slowly unhinged the pen gate to release Duchess and Herb'e into the main arena.

Was this the right thing to do?

I didn't know.

Was I going for it too soon?

I didn't know.

Was Herb'e in the mix?

I didn't know.

But what I did know – and know for certain – was that this action would be a defining moment in the lives of my *Perfect Pair*, so, for better or for worse, in thirty minutes' time, my two star dolphins would once again grace a show arena.

News of my decision travelled fast, and it wasn't long before I spied a pensive Clive Rothwell sitting in the auditorium. The stage was set and there was no turning back.

"Ladies and gentlemen, boys and girls, Europe's two greatest dolphins are back in the spotlight for their first ever show at the West Coast dolphinarium. Can I ask you all to put your hands together and give a big round of applause for the amazing … unrivalled … Duchess and Flippa!"

⟨ 96 ⟩

The thunderous sound of frenzied clapping and stamping feet reverberates around the packed auditorium as a fifteen-hundred strong Joe Public shows its appreciation – a mass of animated, smiling faces led by a visibly excited cheerleader: Clive Rothwell.

"Well, people, just listen to that racket. If that doesn't get you going, then nothing will"

I find myself automatically peering down at Herb'e with breathless anticipation.

"Well, my son, this is it – the big day – the day that all will be revealed. Now, hold … hold …"

Fixing his gaze, I swallow deeply. These next few moments will be crucial. Our entire survival now hinges on this one trick: the opening bows – three jumps that will either blast Herb'e back to reality or send him careering even further into the maze.

Will he … or won't he?

Ever so slowly, I curl my fingers into a fist – an imaginary gauntlet trapping his psyche within my palm.

"Hold … hold … go!"

My arm springs skywards, snapping back my head and channelling my gaze towards the heaving auditorium – and the expectant face of my West Coast manager. Like a telescope, my vision zooms in to magnify – clarify – every line on his face.

I daren't look at my two dolphins, but keep my eyes forward and my chin up …

... besides, there's no need to view the main arena, because Clive Rothwell's jubilant face tells me all I need to know ... Clive's face and the explosive cheers that now emanate from an ecstatic army of onlookers.

No, I don't have to look, because I already know ...

... already know that Herb'e is back.

❧ 97 ❧

So ended the final show of the April Bank Holiday, and although my two stars' performance hadn't scaled the dizzy heights of old, it had proven that they were at least out of the starting blocks.

As expected, Duchess had done the lion's share of the work, whilst poor Herb'e had merely flattered to deceive – a sobering reminder that it would take some considerable time to elevate my stars back to their former glory.

Nevertheless, we'd all managed to get through the bank holidays relatively unscathed, which meant that our prospects now looked good. Shows would all but stop until the commencement of the main season in May, giving me a substantial amount of time in which to nurse Duchess and Herb'e back to health. This adjournment would prove most welcome, not only for my Atlanteans, but also for me, because the lack of sleep triggered by the rigours of the now defunct force-feeds had severely pummelled me down. I was quite literally running on empty.

However, even in my fatigued state, my main goal was still to get Duchess and Herb'e back where they belonged – the top. I was now – more than ever – determined to show the West Coast Management why the dolphin industry held my *Perfect* Pair in such high esteem.

No matter what our problems, I intended to prove to everyone – for once and for all – that Duchess and Herb'e were still the best of the best.

⪡ 98 ⪢

"David, just want to say how much we appreciate what you've done here at West Coast over the bank holiday weekend. We know it can't have been easy for you, especially with all those horrendous force-feeds going on."

I wasn't accustomed to hearing Company managers handing out plaudits, particularly after my experiences with Backhouse – the reason why Clive's seemingly heartfelt praise made me feel more than just a tad uncomfortable.

"Thanks, Clive, much appreciated. It's been a rough ride, but, hopefully, it's behind us now." I gave him a reassuring smile. "So onwards and upwards, as they say."

"Yes, I'll drink to that," Clive agreed thoughtfully, "though I must admit, you had me going for a while. I honestly thought Herb'e wasn't going to make it. But what *was* heartening was how *you* never lost faith … always believed that he'd eventually pull through. Anyway, as you say, it's behind us now, because he's back … or, I should say, *they're* back."

I felt obliged to give him the only answer he wanted to hear. "Yeah, they're back…"

But were they?

To my mind, Clive's assumption couldn't have been further from the truth: my two dolphins still had a long way to go – especially Herb'e. I'd endure many more sleepless nights before I could truly say that this ordeal was over.

Nevertheless, our conversation had opened a window of opportunity to broach another subject – my long overdue pay rise. "By the way, Clive, before you go … I need to talk to you. It's about money … or, rather, the lack of it. Since arriving at West Coast, my expenses have rocketed, a state of affairs that will only get worse when the main season starts. So the crux of the matter is, I need a rise – and a substantial one at that." I exhaled nervously. There, I'd said it – and with no regrets, particularly after what I'd been through.

Clive smirked knowingly. "I must admit, David, we were wondering when the subject of money would raise its ugly head."

Immediately, my defences kicked-in – along with a sudden urge to blurt the words "Well, I *have* been kinda busy" – but I managed to hold my tongue.

"I have to admit that when the West Coast consortium took over your wage bill, they were amazed to see how little City Head Office was actually paying you."

Not the usual remark I'd expect from a manager!

"With your reputation, we honestly expected a salary at least equal to that of our last trainer, Gerry Mansell."

I grimaced. Why was I so surprised? *Backhouse* – the rotten, lousy, devious, penny-pinching sod!

"Anyway, to put your mind at ease, I honestly don't visualise any problems securing your pay rise. You've impressed a lot of people during the short time you've been here – none more so than our West Coast managing director ..."

Praise indeed – the West Coast managing director was equal in all respects to Rogers.

"... who, by the way, has asked if you would be willing to attend the next meeting of our local Rotary Club as guest speaker?"

Rotary Club guest speaker? How could I refuse? Besides being a great honour, this would be a fortuitously-timed spoonful of sugar to further my cause.

Reading my expression, Clive grinned and turned to the door. "Great ... I'll tell him that's a 'go', then. Right, can't hang around – I've got work to do. I'll get the ball rolling and submit your pay request today, because – as always – there will be the obligatory red tape."

What a breath of fresh air Clive Rothwell was turning out to be – and to think how I'd misjudged him.

No doubt about it, things were on the up: Duchess and Herb'e were back in the game – albeit tentatively – and, with no Backhouse around to put the mockers on my pay request, a substantial rise now looked to be on the horizon. Superb news to boost a weary spirit ...

... perhaps I *did* have a future at West Coast after all.

❦ 99 ❧

A full three weeks had passed since Duchess and Herb'e's momentous first show in the West Coast arena. Even so, I still had to keep them on light duties, abandoning all the strenuous tricks for which they'd become famous. They might be performing to a reasonable standard, but that vital spark was still missing.

To add to this, Duchess had taken advantage of Herb'e's vulnerability to seize the mantle of lead dolphin, thus pushing him down the pecking order – a dethronement that would inevitably hinder Herb'e's resolve to make a full recovery. For all our sakes, it was imperative that I thwart this hostile takeover, or she might well break our team forever. Somehow, I had to restore order – the only question was, how?

Arming myself with an overfilled mug of tea and the obligatory pack of cigarettes, I commandeered the driest corner of the kitchen to begin formulating my tactics.

Right, Capello, so what do you know? Well, as always, if there's one thing you've learnt about your dolphins, it's that nothing's ever just black and white.

I sucked hard on my tobacco saviour.

Now, Duchess herself told you that during their fourteen-day illness, she and Herb'e had been away – a bizarre assertion strongly supported by her seemingly having no recollection of those dreadful force-feeds. Then, when you asked after Herb'e, she nonchalantly informed you that he wasn't sure whether he wanted to return to this reality or to move on. Now this confirms your belief that no matter how well Herb'e's physical body might be healing, his psyche is not, which means that one push in the wrong direction could easily send him over the top.

Question is: if you can see this scenario unfolding, then why can't Duchess? Unless, of course, she has an altogether different perspective on the matter …

…

What if dolphins view life and death differently from us humans? That would explain why your Atlanteans constantly show indifference when in the presence of a dying colleague – a phenomenon you've never been able to get your head around.

What if they view their bodies as a mere conveyance – temporary vessels to be discarded when deemed no longer of use? An ethos that could well explain their suicide beachings in the wild. A view of death *not* as an end, but as a new beginning … in which case, you've been totally wrong in your previous evaluation of their attitude …

It's not that they are uncaring; it's simply that they have a different set of beliefs.

Blimey, Capello, what an idiot you've been – some expert you turned out to be!

I sighed resignedly, suddenly transfixed by the blank vista of the kitchen wall.

God, what big egos we humans harbour, especially when we refer to dolphins as "animals", because, without doubt, these beautiful beings are far more than that – far, far more. Dolphins like mine are quite literally the people of the sea – a higher race, totally unshackled from the debilitating morality of humankind.

Remember what Carol said all that time ago at Hendle? "Working here has turned everything I ever thought I knew about dolphins on its head."

Well, you certainly can't argue with her there.

And, on that profound note, I stubbed out my cigarette.

So how do you move forward, then? Well, first, you should stop beating yourself up about what happened to Herb'e during that disastrous transport. It's done and dusted, and you have no choice but to play the cards you've been dealt.

Next, remember that Herb'e left the mind-set of his own accord – most probably because he couldn't bear to be without his precious Duchess. A welcome shot in the arm for you, because the equation remains the same: while you have Duchess, you have him.

As for which one of them will eventually be in charge, well, that's anyone's guess. All you can do is go with the flow and hope that everything works out – which it usually does …

… after all, Duchess and Herb'e aren't called *The Perfect Pair* for nothing.

❦ 100 ❧

My dominant diva continued to flex her muscles over a dejected Herb'e, causing me to question what was, by now, a three-week old assessment of my team. Up to press, I'd failed miserably in my effort to find the Herb'e of old – a mission that was proving ever more frustrating with the onset of the holiday season.

Public performances were now gaining momentum as the run-up to the cash bonanza feverishly gathered pace. It was impossible not to notice the meteoric change in the town. Overnight, the kiosks littering the promenade underwent a startling metamorphosis, discarding their weathered coats in favour of gaudy, new attire. West Coast pulsated with the beat of a plethora of amusement arcades – a rallying call almost as old as the resort itself – heralding the seasonal migration of an expectant Joe Public. Its onslaught was reminiscent of a cattle drive – a stampeding herd to awaken the hibernating god … MONEY.

As this avaricious plague took hold, the price of everything in the town suddenly skyrocketed. Nothing was spared, be it a loaf of bread, a pint of beer or a place to rest your head. A change that, for me, favoured a blow to the ribs, as not only would the rest I so desperately needed be denied, but so would, I suspected, that substantial pay rise I'd been promised by Clive Rothwell and the West Coast Management.

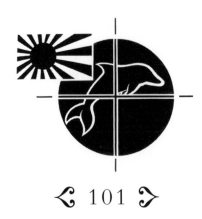

❦ 101 ❧

What I wouldn't give to experience Herb'e's impish schoolboy sparkle for just one more time, because without it, my *Perfect Pair* has lost its air of greatness and descended into the ranks of lesser dolphins. For me, nothing short of soul-destroying

As if this isn't bad enough, I also have Duchess upping her bid to become team leader, and I'm experiencing serious cash flow problems – appalling when I think how I pulled the Company out of the shit with that record-breaking bank holiday weekend.

I mean, how much more do the men in suits want from me?

How much more can they expect to extract?

It's not right, and it's not fair … it's just not fair.

Thank God for Scouse, because without him, I don't know what I'd do. He's the only one able to cope. In fact, if I'm brutally honest, he's the only reason *I'm* still afloat.

Yet even with Scouse, I can see trouble brewing – particularly where Duchess is concerned. My power-hungry princess has clocked Scouse's strength and tenacity, and has suddenly taken to stalking him – following him, googly eyed, around the pool, which is the last thing any of us want. Especially Herb'e, as any intimacy between Scouse and Duchess would kick him headlong to the bottom of the pecking order – a humiliation he wouldn't be able to handle. Losing his precious partner would almost certainly spell his end, meaning – no matter what – I have to support him, let him know that he's still got a friend. Give him hope.

Hope! Some hope – this feeling of abject despair isn't just consuming

Herb'e, it's dragging me down too. All the warning signs are there – and have been for a while. The steadily-intensifying dull headache, the intermittent loss of balance and, worst of all, that overwhelming feeling of nausea – symptoms that spell just one thing: I am beginning to crack.

❧ 102 ❧

I staggered along the deserted early-morning sea front in a half-comatose state, still suffering from the after effects of the previous night's over-indulgences: my new escape – the drowning of one's sorrows in liquid sin.

We were now a full month into the main season and, although we'd managed to get through the shows successfully, I was still missing Herb'e's all-important *connection*. Even the high-pitched wails and shrieks emanating from the promenade's neon jungle had failed to draw him out – a fact that filled me with a heightened desperation. For me and my amorous princess, the only bright light in our lives was now generated by a blind dolphin who, not so long ago, no one had even counted. However, more incredible still was how this luckless Atlantean had the uncanny ability to generate hope, because, without doubt, that's exactly what he did. He had been my saviour – just as, I suspected, I had been his.

And I do mean *saviour*, because things weren't getting any easier. Due to the never-ending problems arising at the pool, good presenters were hard to keep – graphically illustrated by the departure of the pretty, mini-skirted compère who had proved to be such a blessing during the Easter Bank Holiday weekend. A debilitating loss that once more set in motion the cycle of recruitment and training of new presenters, meaning any idea of taking even one day's leave was out of the question.

It was no good holding off any longer. The position in which I now found myself was intolerable – I was short-staffed and short-changed, so it was time for a long-overdue talk with my elusive manager.

"Hi, David, just popped round to see how things are going."

Talk about my elusive manager! Clive Rothwell's sudden appearance made me wonder just which one of us had the psychic foresight.

"Sorry I haven't visited of late, David, but since the season got going, I've hardly had time to even sit down. Believe me when I say it's been pandemonium out there."

Acknowledging him with a half-hearted smile, I turned silently towards the kettle.

"I've been trying to get to you for some time about compiling a speech for the Rotary Club presentation, because our managing director has booked you in for this month's meeting. He tells me that the talk itself shouldn't take too long – around twenty to thirty minutes at most – to be followed by a quick question and answer session."

Feigning disinterest, I gave a deep sigh and slouched across the kitchen table, all the while maintaining a strict silence. I was vexed that he still hadn't mentioned my pay rise, and I wanted him to know it.

"Yes," he continued brightly, "it should be well worth your while, especially as they always round off the proceedings with a sumptuous à la carte meal – on the house, of course."

Snatching aggressively at my half-empty cigarette packet, I freed a smoke – but he still wasn't getting the hint.

"Oh, and here's something else that might interest you – it's about Hendle. I've heard on the grapevine that your moving here has caused ructions between City Head Office and the safari park management. They're said to be fuming about losing *The Duchess and Flippa Show*, and sick to the back teeth of complaints from disgruntled punters."

There was no disguising Clive's delight: his eyes twinkled at the thought of West Coast – so accustomed to failure – outdoing my old pool. But he wasn't the only one. Although I rigidly maintained my expression of indifference, the vision of a floundering Backhouse gave me more than a warm feeling of satisfaction. Nevertheless, I was acutely aware that this news, no matter how delightful, would have serious ramifications.

Head Office viewed the Hendle dolphinarium as its flagship pool, and any humiliation that it suffered would reflect directly on the executives responsible for running it. They would be quick to look for a scapegoat, and would blame the show's demise not on Rogers' golden boy, Backhouse, but on me.

These men were not the sort of people to endure criticism gladly, and, in light of my previous history, those already gunning for me would be more determined than ever to pay me back.

And when they did, I knew it would be in spades.

❦ 103 ❧

Clive was so full of himself at the thought of getting one over on my old stomping ground that he still hadn't clocked our conflicting body language. He chinked with perverse delight, more reminiscent of a mischievous schoolboy at playtime than a Company manager, meaning it was high time I reminded him that playtime was over.

"Clive, we're now in full season and I've still heard nothing about my promised pay rise. I need to know what's happening."

The tone in which I delivered my statement abruptly curtailed Clive's boyish revelry, plunging the room into stony silence. My direct approach had obviously hit the mark.

"To tell the truth, David, I don't know what the delay is. Our general manager personally cleared your pay rise weeks ago. I know because I was with him when he signed the approval form … Look, to put your mind at ease, when I get back to the office, I'll chase it up. It's probably down to some dozy secretary in wages. In the meantime, stop worrying, and go and enjoy yourself at the Rotary Club. It should make a pleasant change from being stuck in this place all the time."

I wasn't convinced. Clive's warm words of reassurance had already been gobbled up by the screech of inner alarm bells – a warning scream that was very rarely wrong.

❧ 104 ❧

As I battled to keep his attention, the training sessions Herb'e once loved were now deteriorating into a chore – a task made all the more arduous by a strident Duchess, determined to hold on to her newly-acquired crown.

"Come on, Herb'e, pull yourself together and show her who's boss. You're letting her make mincemeat out of you!"

The lethargic way in which Herb'e lifted his head from the water made me wonder if he'd even heard me. Perhaps the magic of his dolphin radio had disappeared forever – nowadays, his ever-predictable reply was to turn meekly away from stage in search of solitary waters.

Soul-destroying. Utterly soul-destroying.

Although Forrester had warned me that Herb'e's recuperation would be a long haul, I couldn't help but believe that, somewhere along the line, we'd missed something – something vital. After all, the true cause of Herb'e's illness had never been officially identified. All we knew was that, following the Hendle transport, he'd been on the verge of pneumonia and suffering from acute anaemia – conditions for which he was now receiving massive doses of multivitamins.

So … could his mystery virus still be present and slowly chipping away at his resolve? If that were the case, during the coming months, this hidden assassin would heap even more misery on both Atlantean and man alike …

Backhouse! Rotten, bloody Backhouse!

Powerless and frustrated, I angrily turned on Duchess.

"And you're not helping, either. You're forcing Herb'e out, and if this carries on, we'll lose what's left of him for good. Is that what you want, Duchess? I mean, is it?"

She flashed me a puzzled look. *"What's wrong, David? Why are you getting so upset?"*

My princess just didn't understand – couldn't comprehend my all too human despair. She and I were just too different: two different leaves from two different trees. Duchess harboured beliefs and a moral code that I still struggled to accept – alien concepts of life and death that still left me troubled.

"You know why I'm upset," I retorted. *"Herb'e's fighting for his life, and all you can do is push him around and run after Scouse! I mean, what's happening to you, Duch? Why are you so eager to dump him? Herb'e needs your help … I need your help."*

Locking onto her eyes, I pensively waited for an answer. Instead, I heard a sound – a ringing, the ringing of a telephone, followed by the drone of a monotone voice rising from the kitchen.

"David, that was Clive Rothwell. He wants you at the main office immediately – says it's urgent."

105

"Urgent ... come immediately," he said ... and to the main office, no less – the hallowed home of West Coast officialdom. I wonder what it's all about? It must be important, because if Clive Rothwell has anything to say, he usually comes to see me, not vice versa. Maybe it's about my long-overdue pay rise – the one I'm still sweating about. Or maybe it's an official thank you for my ultra-successful Rotary Club talk. Well, there's only one way to find out, and that's to climb the stairs, knock on his door and ask.

God, trekking up this staircase is like scaling the north face of the Eiger, that's how steep it is. What's more, I feel like I've stepped into a Charles Dickens' novel. There's no light, except for the glow coming from the glass-panelled door at the top of the stairs, and the dark wooden walls reek of a bygone age. Worst of all, there's a musk pervading the atmosphere – a sense of decay and inevitability.

Horrible ... unnerving ... forbidding ...

Bloody hell! During my time in this job, I've faced-down man-hating penguins, a rebellious sea lion and a testosterone-driven elephant – to say nothing of a psycho dolphin – yet I've *never* felt this intimidated before.

People ... crikey, they really do frighten me!

This is ridiculous! I'm dithering like an idiot outside the office door, rooted to the spot and too afraid to knock. But, thanks to that creaky wooden staircase, Clive already knows I'm here.

"Come in, David. We're ready to see you now."

I don't like the sound of that. Who's "we"?

Well, here goes nothing!

Rogers? Mr Rogers? What the heck's *he* doing here? West Coast is well outside his jurisdiction.

"Please sit down and make yourself comfortable, David." Clive's indicating a chair, but it's impossible not to hear the tension in his voice or clock his awkward body language as he perches uneasily on the edge of his seat – a sure sign that something is amiss.

Time to broker a polite conversation with Rogers. "Hello, sir, it's good to see you again," I lie. "Are you well?"

I sense the air tighten as he reciprocates with a guttural grunt. Instinctively, I know what's coming.

I note how he averts his eyes and shuffles his feet.

Here it comes …

"I've been asked by Mr Rothwell and the West Coast managing director to speak to you personally regarding your recent pay request."

My entire body stiffens.

"I will make this brief. As you are already aware, the Company now deems all dolphinarium staff to be equal. Therefore, I regret to inform you that I cannot, under any circumstances, approve your pay rise."

My heart plummets. So this is it – after all my hard work, all my sleepless nights, I finally have my reward.

Payback time – and even sooner than expected.

Clive's distressed and quick to cut in. "Mr Rogers, please … this non-recognition of trainers has already cost this dolphinarium dearly. It's only since David's arrival that we've started to make good profits – borne out by our record-breaking Easter Bank Holiday takings. Surely, in his case, we can afford to bend Company rules?"

I watch Rogers' face tighten as he struggles to remain impassive. He isn't used to facing challenges, especially not from junior managers.

"I'm sorry, Mr Rothwell, but I'm not willing to break Company policy for anyone."

"Look, Mr Rogers, the truth is, if it hadn't been for David, West Coast would still be in a terrible mess, and – to put it bluntly – it's become blatantly obvious to all that Mr Backhouse's policy of dispensing with trainers isn't working."

I have to hand it to Clive, it takes a lot of bottle to go head-to-head with

Rogers. Nevertheless, in bad-mouthing Rogers' golden boy, he's just committed the cardinal sin. Rogers is practically foaming at the mouth.

"Mr Rothwell, I've said all I'm willing to say on this matter. The rest is now up to David."

The rest is now up to David? I'd have to be a moron not to understand that remark – Rogers has just issued me with an unmistakeable ultimatum, challenging me to resign. And, what's more, Clive knows it.

"Please, Mr Rogers, surely it doesn't have to come to this?"

Obviously, it does, because, without another word, Rogers has jumped to his feet and marched out of the office.

And that, as they say, is that.

Goodnight Vienna.

Audience over.

I stare at Clive in shock, unsure of what to do next.

"Well, I guess that's it, then, Clive. End of story."

He doesn't say anything – can't find the words. And no wonder.

As for me, I now have to make one of the most difficult decisions of my life. All my instincts scream, "Walk out! Pack your stuff! Get into your car, drive away and never look back!"

But how can I?

How can I desert the three most precious people in my life?

How can I leave them to the mercy of money-grabbing suits like Rogers and Backhouse, and still sleep at night?

How? How?

clyde rules

❧ 106 ❧

I've been sitting in this lousy dungeon of a kitchen for nearly two hours, just staring at the walls. So much for Clive's theory of a dozy secretary being to blame – it's been Rogers and Backhouse all the time, like a couple of vipers waiting to strike. I can just imagine the two of them, skulking in the shadows, plotting how to take me down.

"David, thank God you're still here! I came as soon as I could. Are you all right?"

An inane question if ever I heard one.

"No, Clive, I'm not all right. What's more, I'll never be all right while I'm working for a bloody cut-throat Company like this."

Clive keeps schtum, and no wonder. How can he read anything positive into what's just happened?

"Has Rogers left yet, or is he enjoying tea and cakes with your managing director?" A cheap shot, but who can blame me? "God, I'm surprised that Rogers even found time to make it here. After all, it's a long way to travel just to give someone a good kicking."

Clive is white-faced and clearly upset, and the last thing he needs is me giving him any more grief, but right now he's the only suit available, so he's gonna have to take it!

"Look, David, I can't begin to guess how you're feeling, especially after all you've been through. You must feel totally betrayed. But the reason I'm here is to tell you that you're not alone – you've got a lot of friends at West Coast willing to fight your cause."

I'm so angry, I barely hear what he's saying.

"David, why do you think Mr Rogers came here in the first place? He came because he *had* to. Our managing director made it quite clear to City Head Office that he had no intention of doing Mr Rogers' dirty work for him – a decision, I might add, that has caused ructions between our two camps. He's upset too, because he doesn't take kindly to being overruled in his own back yard – especially not by a rival Company executive."

Clive … I still can't hear him – my ears are pounding.

"Don't forget, David, Mr Rogers is officially in charge of the dolphin project, which means that, no matter what we here at West Coast may want, the final word will always be down to him – and only him."

That pounding in my ears has suddenly cut to silence – a soulless, bewildering silence.

"Think, David, think … Please don't do anything rash. Try to consider the ramifications for Duchess and Herb'e … especially Herb'e. That's all I'm asking."

Is Clive's concern genuine, or is he merely covering his back?

I can't help but suspect a little of both.

Anyway, listening time is over – now it's my turn.

"Don't you think I've already done that, Clive? Believe me when I tell you that my dolphins are the only reason why I haven't already walked. I'm not here for the Company, and I'm not here for you. I'm here for Duchess, Herb'e and Scouse, and that's all, because it's abundantly clear that I'm the only one who gives a toss about them.

"We both saw what happened during that meeting: Rogers handed me an ultimatum. He didn't give two hoots about my dolphins – all he cared about was getting rid of me. I mean, just look at the risk he was willing to take – chaos, loss of revenue … and almost certain dolphin deaths. No, Clive, none of that was of the slightest importance to him – the only thing paramount was making *me* disappear. As you said yourself, he's even fallen out with your managing director over it …

"I'm sorry, Clive, but no matter how much support you and your people give me … I'm living on borrowed time."

He's gone quiet and his eyes have dropped. He knows that I'm right – but my rant hasn't finished yet.

"You know what I found particularly creepy about that meeting, Clive?

The way Rogers mimicked Backhouse – the inflections in his voice, his condescending manner. Even his gestures were the same. It was like he'd been cloned.

"Remember, I worked with Backhouse for a long time, so know just what he's capable of. Believe me, he's utterly devious – like a cancer – corrupting everyone and everything he gets near. No one's safe – Rogers being a prime example. Backhouse has poisoned him.

"When I first met Rogers, he was known for his charm and courtesy – the epitome of old-school management. Now look at him … look what he's become – nothing more than Backhouse's nasty, vindictive, little puppet.

"A word of warning, Clive – one you'd do well to heed: Mr Rogers is not the problem. Backhouse is – and always has been! So, whatever you do, keep your distance, because if you allow him to get close, he'll knife you in the back – something our mutual friend Mr Rogers has yet to discover."

❧ 107 ☙

Outbluffed and outplayed, I was barely hanging in the game.

Due to Herb'e's continuing poor health, I'd lost my most precious card – my *Perfect Pair*. Their sudden and unceremonious fall from grace had stripped my Atlanteans of their worth, depositing them, like me, on the expendable list. A plight made even more fraught by Rogers having pulled rank on the West Coast hierarchy, effectively leaving my team and me vulnerable to the whims of the City Head Office.

Despite this, any reports of my imminent demise from the seaside dolphinarium would have been grossly exaggerated, particularly in light of what I'd learned during that fateful meeting. It had been glaringly obvious that the West Coast Management had no inkling of the *real reason* for my transfer from Hendle.

Incredible as it might seem, my altercation with Backhouse had never been disclosed – not even to the City Head Office executives. It had been surreptitiously swept under the carpet to avoid any loss of face, leaving Rogers to explain away the Hendle troubles as a minor "clash of personalities".

And who would question him? Particularly as the only other executive then present had been Will Chadderton – a man who had since mysteriously disappeared from the Company ranks. Fortuitous to say the least, as, with my old Hendle manager gone, no one would ever know the damning truth.

No one would know how, on the night of that Hendle pool ditch, Backhouse had chosen to walk, abandoning four distressed dolphins in toxic holding pens – a gross dereliction of duty that Rogers had helped to cover up.

Little wonder they both wanted me gone!

108

Despite the support of the West Coast fraternity, I was still looking down the barrel of a gun. Recent events had convinced me that the career I'd once naively described as my "dream job" was fast coming to an ignominious end. Yet despite this, I knew that I still had an important task to perform. Wounding as it would be, I had to prepare my charges for a life without me.

Years of thought-based training had left my Atlanteans vulnerable, with psyches deliberately moulded to respond only to me – a defensive conditioning that would quickly become their curse. I would now have to try to undo what had taken years to perfect – a near impossible task.

Even more disturbing, time was short. I figured I'd only have until the end of the season at best to put my affairs in order, because, after that, the Company would be keen to embark on its ghastly wintering policy – a Backhouse obscenity that I had absolutely no intention of implementing.

This confrontational standpoint meant that I had backed myself into a corner. Rogers and Backhouse were under no illusions as to my aversion to any notion of wintering at Hendle and, in view of recent events, would be loath to ask me to reconsider. So, come what may, by the end of the West Coast season, I would be up the proverbial creek without a paddle – in other words, gone! An inevitability that recalled yet another saying: no one is indispensable.

An idiom that the Company would learn – to its cost – to be untrue.

During the weeks that followed, a surreal atmosphere cloaked the dolphinarium – a penetrating, soulless emptiness that reeked of defeat. This air of capitulation quite literally touched everyone, none more so than Clive, who suddenly stopped visiting – a stark change of behaviour that also extended to the rest of the West Coast hierarchy. None of them needed reminding of their humiliation.

Although this change of heart was to be expected, it still stung, as it meant that I was again alone. But on a positive note, if you could call it that, this cold-shouldering now allowed me to concentrate on those who *actually* needed me – my Atlanteans.

The power struggle between Duchess and Herb'e was continuing unabated, with Duchess striving to muscle Herb'e out. Nonetheless, I continued to reward both dolphins equally, as it was imperative that I keep them performing as a team.

"Together, Duchess, remember, always together! This isn't a one-dolphin show."

Obviously still feeling the effects of his mystery virus, Herb'e did little to help his cause, choosing to fall tamely into the background during shows – a trait that was no longer acceptable. It was imperative that he fight his corner, as any forced split could finish him. Herb'e reminded me of a china doll: fragile and liable to break at any time.

To make matters worse, Duchess was still pursuing Scouse – a situation that only a few months ago, I would have been the first to make light of. However, it was now becoming a worry. To Duchess, my proverbial ugly duckling had miraculously turned into a handsome swan … and a serious prospect to replace her ailing partner. My Atlantean princess obviously had a liking for strong males.

Thankfully, her ardour was not welcomed by Scouse, who now spent virtually all his time hiding in pool corners – difficult, at best, as the pool wasn't that big.

"Looks like you've got yourself a girlfriend, Scouse ... whether you want one or not."

Poor Scouse! It was obvious that he wasn't used to female attention.

"Well, I don't want a girlfriend! Tell her to go away and leave me alone."

"I wish it was that easy, lad, I really do. But you know what females are like ..."

Trembling, he rushed to the pool's furthest point and pushed his head against the wall. The poor little fella was scared stiff ... Maybe he didn't know what females were like after all.

Either way, I couldn't stand idly by and watch him suffer any longer.

"Come on, Scouse, into the holding pen for a couple of days. It's the only way you're gonna get any peace."

Although two days stuck in the cramped confines of a pen might sound extreme, it was quite literally the only way to take Scouse off the menu. Nevertheless, I couldn't help but feel guilty.

"I'm sorry, Scouse ... I'm really, really sorry ... but it's for your own good."

Vigorously rubbing his melon, I tried to jolly him up by playing the comedian.

"That's what you get for being so irresistible to the ladies!"

Immediately, a blowhole-powered blast erupted fully into my face, leaving me dripping in a slimy, watery mucous ... Yuk!

"And that's what YOU get, Dave, for trying to be funny!"

❦ 110 ❧

The clank of prison bars effectively put an end to love's young dream – if only for a short time – giving me the chance to have an uninterrupted talk with my *Perfect Pair.*

"Right, you two, holidays are over. It's about time we officially went back to training sessions, because we all need a boost. That especially goes for you, Herb'e. I know you don't feel one hundred per cent, but I can't allow you to continue drifting through shows. You're supposed to be part of a team, and team players don't let their partners do all the work. So let's drop the 'I don't care' routine and get back into the game."

Some might call this lecture harsh – terse and unfeeling – but I believed it to be necessary. The time for pleasantries was over.

Unperturbed by my tone, Duchess pushed her head onto my knees.

"As for you, Duch, Herb'e's your partner, and you need to start showing some loyalty. He's going through a bad time, and the last thing he needs is you screwing around with Scouse."

Duchess abruptly slipped back into the water – message received loud and clear. But I wasn't done with her yet.

"So, Duch, forget about Scouse and concentrate on putting this show back where it belongs – at the top."

Not simply idle words, particularly after what had happened with Rogers. It was time to remind the head of the dolphin project – along with the rest of his cronies – just why my team and I were considered to be the best of the best!

❦ 111 ❧

The next fifteen days saw the resumption of those all-important nightly training sessions – phase one of our fight back.

These workouts mirrored those of old: me, Duchess and Herb'e – alone, up-close and personal, preventing any onlookers from corrupting our bond.

My strategy took the form of a three-pronged attack:

First, despite his fragile condition, I had to bring Herb'e back into the fold, as this was the only way to cool Duchess' ardour for Scouse. It would also help check her continuing attempt at a hostile takeover.

Second, I had to initiate a strict training regime, where solo performances would not be tolerated under any circumstances … All for one, and one for all!

Third, I had to seriously change my way of thinking. I couldn't allow the spectre of Backhouse to intimidate me any longer. I needed to get back to basics. Create a goal to give myself focus. In other words, get payback against a treacherous City Head Office. And there was only one way to achieve this: the resurrection of Europe's greatest team – Duchess and Herb'e … *my* Duchess and Herb'e.

The bit was firmly between my teeth and, despite the obligatory daily shows, I managed to maintain the momentum of our late night training sessions, painstakingly moulding my *Perfect Pair* back to greatness – a mission that saw me virtually living at the dolphinarium.

But, unfortunately, the fates again intervened, cruelly manifesting their handiwork during one of my early morning visits …

… Herb'e – a lump the size of a cricket ball protruding from the side of his neck.

❧ 112 ❧

"Hello, is that Tony Forrester? It's David at West Coast. You need to get down here right away. It's Herb'e – he's got a huge abscess on the side of his neck ... and I do mean huge."

Got to slow down ... catch my breath.

"It came up overnight. I've never seen anything like it. Believe me, Tony, I'm not exaggerating when I say it's literally the size of a cricket ball."

God, poor Herb'e! No wonder he's been feeling so rough. All that poison trapped inside him ...

Poison ... Backhouse ... Backhouse ... rotten, bloody Backhouse! This would never have happened if ...

No, Capello! No! You've got to stop doing this ... you've got to get that rat out of your head ...

Rat ... Backhouse ... Backhouse ... rotten, bloody Backhouse!

"David, are you still there?"

A grunt is all Forrester's gonna get.

"For a moment, I thought we'd been cut off. Anyway, try not to panic. I'll soon be on my way. Time is of the essence, so I'll need Herb'e penned and ready for examination as soon as I get there."

"Okay, Tony, but don't forget about the shows ... Tony ...? Tony ...?"

He's gone!

Well, that conversation was short and sweet. Still, all that matters is he's on his way – and the sooner the better.

Amazing, I still can't believe the size of Herb'e's lump ... Or just how quickly it came up. Yet it doesn't seem to be affecting him. He's swimming around like he hasn't got a care in the world – like he doesn't even know it's there. I wonder … maybe, just maybe, this is what we've been waiting for – the first visible sign of Herb'e's mystery illness … an insidious poison finally coming to a head. God, I hope so, I really do!

Still, I'm no vet, so it's no good me speculating. It's down to Forrester now. Either way, it's obvious that I can't work Herb'e again – not until we know exactly what we're dealing with. So it looks like we're back to one-dolphin shows – just Scouse and me. That should make me popular with the men in suits.

Still, do I give a damn about Management? No! Because for the first time in months, I've been gifted a spark of hope … hope of getting my old friend back.

Blimey! I must've looked at that clock at least twenty times and I've only just put down the receiver. This is unbearable!

Come on, Forrester, get those wheels turning and get down here fast. We've got work to do.

True to his word, Forrester arrived later that morning – annoyingly, just as I was about to walk on stage for the first performance of the day. Lousy timing, as we were now playing to packed audiences with only a thirty-five-minute window in which to turn them around.

This clash with full houses meant that Herb'e's so-called emergency examination had to be put on hold, as whilst there was money to be made, Management would not permit the cancellation of shows. For the remainder of the day, Forrester would have to adopt the role of spectator – on full pay, of course.

Herb'e's ballooning abscess had again placed my *Perfect Pair* on the sick list, leaving my ever-reliable Scouse to pick up the pieces. However, as feared, the return to a one-dolphin show proved extremely unpopular with senior Management, who were quick to call for the break-up of my two stars, citing high season as justification for the split.

However, this was a demand that Clive Rothwell knew I would never implement, as to do so would destroy my team. So, on top of everything else, I was now destined to lock horns with an otherwise supportive West Coast hierarchy.

Despite the complication of shows, Forrester managed to juggle a full six days of treatments, until, overnight, the abscess suddenly doubled in size. To most people, this spectacle would have looked nothing short of horrific, but, for us, it was a green light. At last, this poisonous mountain had come to a head, meaning it could now be lanced.

"Right, David," Forrester began, "I'll explain exactly what's going to happen. Once we've got Herb'e penned and lying on the false floor, I'll need you to keep him calm, because this is going to be a long job."

I nodded soberly.

"Then comes the easy bit ..."

Forrester laughed mischievously, which I found decidedly weird, as I'd always believed him to be humourless.

"I'm going to lance the abscess with a scalpel, then dig out all the nasty stuff. Not a pretty sight – so I hope you're not squeamish."

Giving him a beseeching look, I nodded again. "Just before you start, Tony, would it make any difference if I were?"

"No, not really, because Herb'e's need is greater than yours. Still, if you should feel queasy, please be aware that there's a bucket in the corner."

I wasn't sure which was worse, Herb'e's proposed treatment or Forrester's inane attempt at a wisecrack.

Either way, I was about to find out.

❦ 114 ❧

Flashing my ring close to Herb'e's eye, I whispered:

"Once we've got rid of that nasty lump, you'll feel a whole lot better, believe me. So try to be a brave boy while the vet does his work."

Watching Forrester perform his task certainly wasn't for the faint-hearted, and quickly sent green-faced onlookers racing to the toilets.

Once lanced, the gargantuan mound revealed a white, viscous, cottage-cheese-like substance cocooned in a snotty goo. Forrester quite literally proceeded to scoop it out with a spoon, leaving a deep hole in the side of Herb'e's neck that took a full thirty minutes to clean and sterilise.

Meanwhile, throughout the entire ordeal, poor Herb'e lay prostrate, uttering not a sound.

"Come on, lad, hang in there. You'll soon be back in the water ..."

The entire procedure, from lancing to cleaning, took a full hour and a half before he was ready to be released into the main pool – which, to Herb'e, must have seemed like a lifetime.

My stricken Atlantean was not impressed with his treatment: the indignities he'd suffered at the hands of Forrester were quite literally more than he could bear. He bulleted from the holding pen in a fit of rage, frenziedly shaking his head and smashing his tail on the water.

"Hell, Tony, Herb'e's really hacked-off. I mean, just look at him go."

Nevertheless, for the first time since leaving Hendle, I could faintly hear what could only be described as a blasphemous song. Herb'e was *not* a happy bunny, and, although distant, there was no mistaking his angry *connection*. In other words, he was talking again – or, more precisely, swearing.

"Well, Mr Forrester, I don't think we'll be at the top of his Christmas card list this year."

The relieved vet stood beside me, smirking.

"You're right – he's fuming. I certainly wouldn't want to be in the water with him right now. Anyway, apart from the obvious, how do you think the treatment went?"

At first, I didn't answer, only daring to hope. Then, unable to contain my enthusiasm any longer, I broke into a wide smile.

"Not bad … I think we might just have turned a corner. I think there's a good chance that I've just got my old Herb'e back."

115

Herb'e's daily catches and treatments continued for a further week – an utterly draining routine that always ended with a severe temper tantrum. My poor Atlantean was obviously sick to death of repeated manhandling and injections. And who could blame him? Since his arrival at West Coast, this torment had been the only life he'd known.

Distressing as this might be, there was little doubt that Herb'e's strength was returning – and quickly – painfully evidenced by the array of new bruises now covering my body.

Throughout my training career, I'd always held a conviction that the best remedy for the post-viral blues was good old-fashioned hard work. It was also the safest option – particularly when it came to Duchess and Herb'e – as my greatest fear was the sudden return of that dreaded dolphin mind-set. I'd already discovered to my cost how allowing them the luxury of thought could all too easily end in disaster, so, with this in mind, I decided to put my *Perfect Pair* back to work. A welcome decision, not just for a disgruntled Management, but also for a certain weary, blind dolphin who had single-handedly carried the shows.

And, thus, the stage was set for the much-anticipated return of my two stars, lining up side by side to entertain the packed seaside audiences of the West Coast resort.

Did I just say side by side?

Duchess had other ideas.

⟨ 116 ⟩

"Come on, Duchess, the show's only just started and you're giving me grief. How many times do I have to tell you that you and Herb'e must work as a team? Which means no solos."

Duchess was more determined than ever to carry on where she'd left off, with no intention of surrendering her mantle as lead dolphin. I'd always known that this first show would re-ignite their power-struggle. Nevertheless, it had to be resolved – especially for Herb'e, whose fragile psyche was at breaking point. The big question now: how would he cope with the heat of a live show?

There was no arguing that Herb'e's long illness had exacted a heavy toll, leaving him a shadow of his former self. Yet, during the first phase of this performance, I detected a definite mood change – a turnaround.

Herb'e was growing visibly stronger, no longer capitulating tamely to Duchess' bullying. Even more marked was the shift in the feel of our *connection*: although still weak, I sensed an altogether different Herb'e. The consciousness I now encountered was bolder, more determined ... aloof.

"I mean it, Duch, pack it in! You work with him *or not at all."*

The change wasn't just confined to Herb'e – Duchess was different too, as though she'd suddenly realised that the tide was turning against her.

"We don't need Herb'e, David. I'll do the tricks ... Get rid of him!"

Her eyes blazed with fire – or was it panic?

"No, Duchess, that can't happen. It's the three of us or nothing."

Almost immediately, the water at the foot of the stage began to bubble as they wrestled for position.

"That's the spirit, Herb'e. Don't let her get away with it. Show her you're not having it anymore!"

Herb'e's newfound tenacity continued to exert itself throughout the show, and by the time I'd blown the final whistle, he'd more than done himself justice.

To the audience, my feuding team had simply been dolphins behaving badly.

However, I knew differently.

After months in the doldrums, this was Herb'e making his long-awaited comeback, and – although we still had a long road to travel – the resurrection of my *Perfect Pair* was unmistakably back on track.

117

During Herb'e's sickness, I'd continued to feed my Atlanteans equally, despite Duchess having done most of the work. However, now my strategy had changed: I'd imposed a strict disciplinary code, much like that adopted during the late night training sessions – no rewards unless all tricks performed in unison.

This change of tactic didn't go down well with Duchess, whose opposition finally came to a head during one of our busy afternoon shows.

"Please, David, I keep telling you, we don't need Herb'e anymore. It's just you and me now, and I'll prove it by working for nothing."

Then she clattered Herb'e with such ferocity as to send him racing to the sulking corner of the pool – where, unfortunately, he made camp for the remainder of the day.

Ordinarily following a first show disaster, I would immediately swap my show dolphins over, but – in this case – I decided to stay with my defiant diva. I had to admire her audacity, as working without reward would be a huge sacrifice to make.

Could I afford to miss this opportunity to find out just how far her love for me would stretch?

Would she indeed work all day for no reward as promised?

With any other Atlantean, my answer would have been no, but with Duchess, I wasn't so sure. The *connection* she and I shared was unique – truly special. So, with four shows still to be completed, I again asked myself – how much would she be willing to sacrifice?

True to her word, Duchess performed the remaining shows without asking for one single fish. And, what's more, she seemed to relish it – a sad state of affairs for poor Herb'e, who remained subserviently in the corner with his back to the stage.

"See, David, I told you I'd do it. I'll never let you down! Never!"

What on earth was I gonna do?

Her love.

His heartbreak.

Not for the first time, I found myself trapped between a rock and a hard place.

Then came that familiar, sweet-smelling nausea as my psyche melted into the intimacy of her *connection*.

She and I together on stage …

Her greatest dream … her foremost desire … her ultimate triumph …

… a stage without Herb'e.

❧ 118 ❧

What a lousy excuse for a holiday resort this place is. I mean, who in their right mind would actually want to come here? Since arriving in this rotten, filthy hole, I've had so many downers, it's untrue, and now – just to top it off – I've got to put up with daily shows that have deteriorated into nothing more than a slugfest.

It's soul-destroying seeing Duchess and Herb'e like this. I feel like a referee sandwiched between two backstreet brawlers. Even worse, I can't understand why it's happening, because, deep down, I know that the struggle for lead dolphin is nothing more than an excuse – a smokescreen for something else … something darker. God, it's as if they don't recognise each other anymore. Yet how can that be? They've been together forever.

I clearly remember what the young American transporter told me back at North Liston: how Herb'e refused to leave Duchess after her capture; how he sacrificed his own freedom to stay by her side – quite literally birthing my legendary *Perfect Pair.*

So how has it come to this?

No matter, I can't allow it to continue. Somehow, I must end it. I'm already at full stretch with the mind games – psychic duels that leave me so drained I literally stagger off stage. If this carries on for much longer, it won't be a case of staggering off stage, but collapsing *on* it.

Yet I have to hang in there – get a grip – because I'm just as determined as my two Atlanteans to get my way. I've worked too bloody hard to lose it all now …

I want my team back …

I want the shadow ballet back …

… *my* shadow ballet – the routine we left behind all those months ago at Hendle …

And, what's more, I intend to have it.

❦ 119 ❧

The winning back of my team would undoubtedly be my last big play, so it was imperative that I get it right.

Strange as it may seem, the physical violence now unfolding between my two Atlanteans would require sensitive handling. I had to ensure that neither one of them tasted humiliation, which would mean sticking to my original plan of equal rewards.

This was going to be tough as far as audiences were concerned, because the upcoming shows wouldn't be pretty – or, for that matter, popular with Management.

However, even I could not have foreseen for just how long I'd have to hold this line …

… or, for that matter, what would happen next.

120

A full ten days had passed before the fighting finally subsided and a truce begrudgingly called. My charges had at last been forced to accept the inevitable – come what may, they were stuck with each other.

Incredibly, the first few days of this fragile peace threw up something wholly unexpected – believe it or not, a blossoming romance. After months of quite literally battering holes out of each other, Duchess and Herb'e finally got it together, flirting outrageously by swimming belly-up to invite sex play – XXX games that reaffirmed Duchess' liking for strong males.

This was particularly good news for Scouse, who was less than skilled in the art of fending off amorous young females. He, more than anyone, was grateful that normal service had been resumed.

But had it?

I couldn't shake the feeling that things were not what they seemed. Although Herb'e's strength had returned, his once-razor-sharp *connection* had not: I could hear him, but it was as if he were speaking from a distant room. Further, he was lacking that mischievous banter of old, which – for me – transformed the dolphin now courting Duchess into an unfamiliar entity: a complete stranger.

To doubt my instinct would be stupidly optimistic, as it had been proven correct on too many occasions. Even so, I prayed that this time I'd got it wrong – hopelessly wrong.

121

Hello! Well, here's a pleasant surprise – the return of a fair-weather friend, or, should I say, fair-weather manager.

"Fantastic show, David, absolutely fantastic! It's good to see Duchess and Herb'e back on song again."

Now there's a happy man, if ever I saw one. Clive's literally bubbling over with enthusiasm.

"Great to see that you've brought back the jump tricks, because the punters really appreciate them – especially the camera buffs."

They're not the only ones – there was a time when I thought I'd never see a highball performed again. Duchess and Herb'e's comeback can't be overplayed. In fact, when you come to think of what they've been through, it's little short of miraculous.

"I still can't believe that I'm actually standing here in *my* dolphinarium watching them perform. It's incredible!"

That sudden space in time – that awkward silence – a sure sign that Clive has something else on his mind.

"Er … David, now that your team is on the mend, do you think there's any chance we'll ever see the shadow ballet? After all, that's what they're famous for, isn't it?"

Can you believe it? Typical Management logic if ever I heard it. Still, no good getting my knickers in a twist, because Clive has a point. If Duchess and Herb'e are strong enough to jump through hoops and over hurdles, then they're strong enough to attempt the somersault routine.

"I'm not making any promises, Clive, but I'm gonna try to introduce the shadow ballet sometime next week. I won't know for certain just how far I can push them until this week's shows are done and dusted."

The one thing I've learned about Clive is that he can't hide his feelings, which makes him unlike any other executive I've ever known. I mean, his face has just lit up … God! How *did* he ever become a manager?

"Great! That's great, because everyone wants to see it performed – none more so than me. Even better, news of Duchess and Herb'e's recovery has sent our pre-bookings through the roof, so you can expect to be a very busy man."

Expect to be? Expect to be? I'm always busy … In fact, I never stop!

"David, we all know what a kick in the teeth it must have been when Mr Rogers refused your pay request, but, if it's any consolation, I want you to know that our managing director has resubmitted it – so all is not lost."

Poor Clive!

Poor West Coast Management!

They're all still blissfully unaware of the *real* reason for my knockback. Rogers and Backhouse have clearly worked overtime to keep their little secret. Well, I owe them nothing, so it's about time I put the record straight.

"I really appreciate what you and your MD are trying to do for me, Clive, but the truth is, you're both wasting your time. There's no way in a million years that Rogers is ever gonna listen."

That shook him – the smile on his face has just slipped down to his feet.

"Tell you what, Clive, why don't you pull up a chair while I put the kettle on. You and me are gonna have a long overdue chat – and you won't *believe* what I've got to tell you."

Now, where the heck have I left my cigarettes?

122

It's inconceivable how some minds work, how certain individuals actually think. For months, I'd been put through hell, yet I'd guarded the antics of my two tormentors with verve – something that beggared belief.

Why in the world had I been so complicit? Was it out of misguided loyalty to an industry I'd once loved? Or was it down to some outdated respect for authority figures?

In truth … maybe it was both – especially in Rogers' case. He was a person I'd always respected, and – even now – found hard to paint as bad. Nevertheless, with his underhand agenda now revealed, I was under no illusions as to how this misguided man would react. Shadow ballet or no shadow ballet, I would pay the price for the infidelities of my loose lips.

As for Clive, having heard my account, he'd hurriedly scampered off with his tail firmly between his legs. Not unexpected, as he was all too aware of the ramifications my story might have for the dolphin project.

However, during our little talk, I'd purposely kept him in the dark about the work done on Duchess and Herb'e's somersault routine. The shadow ballet was a go … in fact, it had already been performed behind closed doors. I did not intend to donate this unique series of tricks cheaply.

Duchess and Herb'e's fabulous dream movement would undoubtedly be our crowning moment and would demand the greatest audience I could muster …

… a glittering showstopper that the Company's Cinderella pool – the West Coast dolphinarium – would have the honour of hosting.

❧ 123 ❧

Over the coming weeks, the seaside crowds flocked in their droves to see my two magnificent Atlanteans. What's more, Duchess and Herb'e didn't disappoint, mesmerising the wide-eyed holidaymakers with their unrivalled somersault routine – a shadow ballet of exquisite grace and beauty, performed, as always, in absolute unison.

To the unknowing eye, my dream team was now back to its brilliant best; yet no matter how upbeat *I* tried to play it, I found it impossible to dispel that gnawing foreboding. To my mind, the alien Herb'e who now rolled through the air was quite literally a disaster waiting to happen. He reminded me of a beautiful, porcelain figure – fragile and waiting to break …

… waiting to break …

… waiting to break my heart …

…

I was under no illusions as to his vulnerability. He needed kid-glove treatment, as any shift in his equilibrium might trigger his demise.

In contrast to the apparent mood of celebration at the West Coast arena, the resurrection of my *Perfect Pair* didn't sit well with City Head Office. Duchess and Herb'e's rip-roaring success was again being viewed as a slap in the face for the Company's premier pool, Hendle – a dolphinarium that had never recovered from our expulsion.

For Rogers and Backhouse, our West Coast triumph was a huge embarrassment as it reignited the displeasure of an already disgruntled Hendle Safari Park management

However, the controversy surrounding my super team wasn't confined to

Hendle alone – West Coast had been affected too. Its managing director was furious at Rogers' hard-line stance against his repeated request for my pay rise, and as the two leaders locked horns, the once friendly banter they had shared quickly descended into conflict.

Further, on learning of my altercation with Backhouse, the West Coast hierarchy had at last realised the true motivation behind Rogers' animosity towards me. They were also well aware of what would happen should he succeed in driving me out. Duchess, Herb'e and Scouse would automatically down tools, causing the shows to suffer a complete and irreversible collapse. Their thriving dolphinarium would again descend into chaos.

I'd always known that the re-emergence of my *Perfect Pair* would leave Rogers and Backhouse smarting, but never dreamt that they'd allow their blinkered desire for vengeance to jeopardise an entire Company venue. After all, they were executives and duty-bound to protect Company profits.

Incredibly, I'd grossly miscalculated their loyalty to their money deity. Spurred-on by the manipulative Backhouse, Rogers now viewed the supportive West Coast dolphinarium as a sacrificial lamb.

My days of rocking the boat were fast ending – no matter what I achieved, come the close of season, my feet literally wouldn't touch the ground.

❧ 124 ❧

Despite my approaching end of days, the welfare of my charges proved to be an ongoing trial. Although shows were more than running smoothly, I was permanently aware of the challenge that Herb'e posed. My belief in never allowing my Atlanteans any time to think was now more pertinent than ever – especially in light of the successful reintroduction of their shadow ballet. It was imperative that I keep my *Perfect Pair* engaged, which meant presenting them with a new goal.

For some time, I'd toyed with the idea of adding an exciting extension to their somersault routine. A true spectacular of my own creating – a double forward somersault tail highball!

The vision had already been seeded. The props for this trick would consist of a thirteen-foot pole with a netted beach ball hanging from each end. This pole would be attached to a pulley, allowing it to be raised approximately sixteen feet towards the roof of the dolphinarium.

The trick would entail Duchess and Herb'e performing a full forward somersault before hitting the balls with their tails – a fabulous spectacle, never before seen.

Although the training of this extravaganza would be physically tiring for all concerned, it would be the *perfect* remedy for Herb'e. Introducing this trick would act as a double-edged sword, bringing us closer together as well as keeping our minds busy. It was crucial that I keep my alien dolphin occupied.

Nevertheless, I still couldn't shake the horrible feeling that the wheel was about to fall off. I'd brought my *Perfect Pair* back to their former greatness, and the show was a winner …

So what was my problem? Why was I so anxious?

❦ 125 ❧

Amazingly, Herb'e achieved the double forward somersault tail highball within three weeks, with Duchess, as customary, lagging just behind. Always the perfectionist, I stubbornly resisted any temptation to slot the trick into the show prematurely, purposely holding it back until they could perform it in unison. Important, as this fabulous new extension to the shadow ballet would effectively be my last bite of the cherry, so it needed to be right.

Nevertheless, I had to get a move on as the fates were unpredictable, and, given the opportunity, might be tempted to add a twist to our crowning moment.

I'd always dreamed that when my final exit came, I would go out in a firestorm of rebellion, exposing the business for what it was – starting with the public shaming of the head of the dolphin project, Rogers, to be swiftly followed by the televised drowning of the conniving Backhouse.

Glorious in the extreme!

So how did it go so wrong?

How could the catalyst for our destruction have come from something so utterly mundane?

An everyday dolphinarium commodity that I'd always taken for granted …

How?

⟨ 126 ⟩

"Fish … Fish? What do you mean you're running out of fish? You received a brand new delivery only today. I know because I signed for it myself."

Typical Management response – the only thing Clive knows about a fish is that it has gills, fins and a tail.

"I know you signed for it, Clive, because I've got the full consignment sitting here on the kitchen floor. Problem is, it's all rotten! Completely inedible! The slab of herring I thawed this morning has all but turned to mush. I'm telling you, Clive, there's no way in the world that the dolphins will eat this. It's bad fish – plain and simple!"

"Look, David, we've never had any trouble with the fish before. Surely, you can make do? I mean, can't you mix it with mackerel or something? After all, a fish is a fish, isn't it?"

Something tells me that getting through to Clive is gonna be a long haul, 'cause all he's done so far is reaffirm what I already know – that he hasn't got a bloody clue.

"Clive, you're *not* listening. The thawed herring is actually scale shedding, and the belly roe stinks. It's obvious that the suppliers are having problems with their herring stocks, so are buying-in inferior fish from other sources. So to answer your question – no, we *can't* make do! I need the lot changing, and I need it changing today, so you're gonna have to tell 'em to replace it!"

There it is again. That awkward space in time – that unmistakeable silence that screams he's not impressed.

239

"Oh, and just to make your morning even better, we've only got five days at most of our original stock left, so you'll need to get your skates on."

I suppose that deep sigh at the end of the line indicates that our conversation is at an end. One thing's for sure, Clive didn't hang around to exchange niceties.

Still, who cares? All that matters is that he's *got* the message – because the last thing I need right now is a fish problem.

127

All that arm-twisting just to get the fish suppliers to change that consignment of bad herring, then they go and land us with another batch that's even worse. Are they taking the Mickey or what? Well, I'm not 'avin' it! By my reckoning, I only have a day's worth of good herring left. After that, I'm up shit creek without a paddle.

I can't afford to give Herb'e an excuse to stop working, because if that happens, he'll stop eating. And if Herb'e stops eating, so will Duchess – and, in all probability, Scouse too. Can't hang around anymore … It's time to act – personally call the fish company's distribution manager and tell him what the score is.

Going over Clive's head like this isn't gonna make me popular. Still, as he's *again* been noticeable by his absence, I don't see any other way.

"I'm sorry, but the head of our distribution department isn't available to take calls this morning. Can I help?"

That's all I need – can't get to the cook, so have to deal with the bottle washer.

"It's about the last two batches of fish sent to the West Coast dolphinarium …"

…

God! I've been trying to get through to her for ages – to explain what an impossible situation I'm in. But she's just not listening. It's like talking to a brick wall. All I'm getting is some sales pitch.

"We have a very strict quality control to ensure that only the finest fish reaches our customers. Further, we …"

Unbelievable! She sounds like a recording, every word meticulously delivered as if she's reading from a customer care manual. Why won't she listen? Why won't *anyone* listen? I want an explanation – and, by heck, I'm gonna get one!

...

"Mr Capello, as you have already inferred, we are indeed experiencing difficulties with our herring stocks. You must appreciate that we supply our seafood products to all the top restaurants in the area – fish meant for human consumption. We have to prioritise, and since your order is for animal feed ... I'm sure you understand."

Understand! *Understand!* I knew it – knew that something underhand was going on. All that flashy talk, just to cover up for a company offloading substandard fish – herring unfit for human consumption. Well, if it's unfit for humans, it's *certainly* unfit for my Atlanteans.

There's no point in talking to this bimbo any longer. I have to get back to Clive and demand that he put his foot down – preferably on their heads. If he doesn't, he won't just lose his precious shows, he could well lose his dolphins too.

For crying out loud! Are the fates ever going to grant me any peace? Or is it their sole intention to torture me forever?

What am I gonna do? There's hardly any good fish left in the freezers, and if it runs out (No! Not *if* it runs out, *when* it runs out!), what the hell's gonna happen to Herb'e?

<C 128 <C

Check checklist:

- Check for even the slightest change in Herb'e's behaviour.
- Check whether Herb'e plays with his fish before swallowing.
- Check all pool sumps for pieces of discarded fish.
- Check the holding pen for signs of fish dumping.
- Check for excess fish oil coating the water's surface.
- Check and double-check for evidence of vomiting.

Six heralds of potential disaster – the visible signs of a forthcoming hunger strike. I'd have to keep my wits about me.

Either way, I was in big trouble: having virtually run out of good herring, I was now being forced to mix my Atlanteans' feeds with mackerel, an unpopular substitute that they'd endure only in small doses.

I was a bag of nerves. Every show felt like a tightrope walk, watching and waiting to see just how long it would take before my charges refused their feeds.

It was a full two days before my worst fears materialised: the food intake of all three dolphins suddenly crashed, triggering the beginnings of a Herb'e hunger strike.

My heart plummeted. Nevertheless, despite my constantly harassing them, Clive and the fish suppliers continued to play for time.

"David, I've spoken to the seafood company on numerous occasions, and they still maintain that there's nothing wrong with the fish. However, I've stressed the seriousness of our situation, and they've assured me that they're working hard to source new herring."

Poor, naive, gullible, likeable Clive … out of his depth as the fish company blinded him with science in an effort to protect its reputation – a ring fence that was now propelling my dolphins and me down the path towards destruction.

Herb'e's refusal to feed would almost certainly further the resolve of Duchess and Scouse to do likewise – a process that would be hard to break, even *should* a delivery of good herring eventually arrive. I was quite literally at the end of my tether. Herb'e's dreaded mind-set had again been activated, a mental conviction that would battle hard to possess him.

Deep down, I felt it strike … that despairing scream that ripped through my soul.

❧ 129 ❧

Where was that Biblical miracle I so craved? Would it never come? Or was it merely waiting in the wings to make its grand entrance?

Either way, I couldn't afford to delay. My intuition was deafening in its demand for action. I had to call the vet – and fast.

In the meantime, I set about trying to find some good fish. Herb'e's frailty meant that his condition was likely to deteriorate rapidly, so, in sheer desperation, I contacted some of the local fishermen who worked out of the West Coast harbour.

As always when needing help, the word "dolphin" had the desired effect, and when the boats pulled into port later that day, they were laden with live fish. But there was a problem: the catch consisted mainly of mackerel – a fish my Atlanteans didn't like. Nevertheless, this live haul gave me an idea.

Since their capture, my charges had never encountered living fish, so the sight of them actually swimming around their arena might well work the oracle. I knew this was a long shot, but I couldn't stand idly by while Herb'e faded away.

To add to my woes, I was again experiencing trouble maintaining the water quality, which meant I was having to work on higher chlorine levels – a fact that would be detrimental to my upcoming experiment. Regardless of this, following the final show of the day, I immediately released the live mackerel into the pool.

All I could do now was pray – pray that my Atlanteans' natural curiosity would play to my advantage.

I could hardly breathe. Would they or wouldn't they take the fish?

This would literally be the last throw of the dice, because if it didn't work, it would be back to those horrific force-feeds – a nightmare scenario that my battered psyche couldn't endure again.

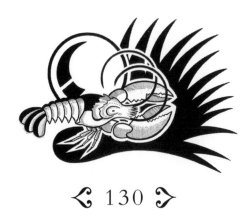

❦ 130 ❧

I felt my toes curling around the pool edge, my vision focussed on every sideways flick of the doomed fish's tails ... hoping against hope.

"Come on, people, at least have a go. Look ... just look! Live mackerel actually swimming around your pool – you'll never get another chance like this."

The barred prey had been in the pool for less than five minutes, yet I already knew that it was hopeless. Instead of chasing the fish, my three charges chose to hang back warily, waiting for them to die.

I watched forlornly as, one-by-one, the stricken fish succumbed to the inevitable chlorine poisoning. The unfortunate mackerel had survived for less than an hour – a stark foretaste of my dolphins' inescapable destiny.

Dolphinariums ... rotten, bloody dolphinariums!

For sheer stupidity, this act had to take the biscuit. How could I have thought that such a hare-brained scheme would actually work?

All I could do now, besides wait for the vet, was remove the dead fish and the twenty or so burly fishermen who had come to watch.

My situation was getting worse by the minute. I had Duchess and Herb'e refusing to eat; no quality fish with which to initiate force-feeds; and I was back to a one-dolphin show, courtesy of Scouse – performances that could collapse at any time.

My world was imploding. The relentless pressure of the last eight months had finally pushed me over the edge. I didn't need a psychiatrist to tell me that I was having another nervous breakdown – I already knew.

I was fog-bound, my mind in turmoil, its banshee wail screeching, "He's dying ... Herb'e's dying ... Run away and hide! Escape!"

I drew on my breath.

"Herb'e's dying … Herb'e's dying …"

There, I'd said it – finally acknowledged what I'd fought so hard to deny. Herb'e's dying … Herb'e's …

"Good news, David, the fish company has just been on the 'phone to say that a consignment of best herring will be with you today."

Somewhere a million miles away, I thought I caught the sound of Clive's voice.

"Yes, they tell me that we can expect a delivery around five-ish."

If the situation hadn't been so utterly desperate, Clive's announcement would have been funny. At long last, I'd got the news I'd been praying for … Just a pity about the timing.

"Yeah, good news, Clive … Only trouble is, it's arrived too late for Herb'e, because the damage is already done. Still, the vet should be delighted, because now he'll have something decent to perform the double force-feeds with. There's no way he could have done it with the crap I've had to work with this week."

And so it began …

131

"Now, where are they? Where the hell have I left …?"

Thank goodness! There they were, lying on the table and hidden beneath a veil of glistening salt crystals – my tobacco comforters.

Finally, the day's shows were over, and, despite more than a few scary moments, my ever-dependable Scouse had carried me through. It was incredible to think just how many times my unsung hero had pulled me out of the mire, yet, even after all he'd done, he was still considered by those with short memories to be damaged goods.

Sucking vigorously on my damp cigarette, I settled back in the chair to wait for Forrester, only to find myself once more drawn into the blankness of the kitchen wall.

We were now halfway through the West Coast season, giving our resident water nymph plenty of time in which to create her latest masterpiece. Due to the relentless damp of our dungeon kitchen, the wall's shoddily-painted surface had cracked to reveal what could only be described as a delicate, spidery artwork – wispy, brown webs that crept from every corner. What a pitifully sad excuse for a restroom this truly was.

Stubbing out my cigarette, I buried my head in my hands.

What was I even doing here?

How could I carry on?

The dynasty of my *Perfect Pair* was racing to an ignominious end, as was my career in the dolphin world. The enchanted mirror that had so bewitched me in those early days was gone, gone forever, its magic drowned in a concrete basin … along with my dreams.

How could all that expectation, all that ambition, have led to this?

"Hello, David – sorry I'm late. The holiday traffic was murder. Still, better late than never. Now, what's the problem?"

I couldn't help but find Forrester's jovial manner irritating, especially after all I'd been through.

"Tony, Duchess and Herb'e haven't eaten for almost three days. Before you say anything, I know that you're gonna recommend force-feeding … but I have to tell you that when it comes to Herb'e, we'll be wasting our time. Herb'e's dying, and no matter how many fish you stuff him with, that's not gonna alter."

Forrester physically froze as my hammer revelation hit him.

"Dying?" he repeated, "Dying? No, David, you're mistaken. Herb'e's not dying … he's probably going through a bad patch. I mean, I've just seen him – he looks a picture of health."

Unlike Philip, Forrester had never believed in the psychic bond I shared with my Atlanteans. He could never appreciate its intimacy, never know how closely linked our minds actually were.

And, whatever else *he* might think, I knew – without doubt – that the endgame had begun.

❧ 132 ❧

As expected, Forrester has insisted on going ahead with the force-feeds, a fruitless procedure that's shredding my nerves.

The pressure is now relentless: two morning catches and force-feeds, five afternoon performances with Scouse – shows that only *I* can make happen – and two more catches and force-feeds to finish the day.

It's terrible ... gut wrenching ... and I don't know how much more I can take. There are no words to describe the hell I'm going through. All my inner strength has gone – drained away – and I feel like I'm about to implode. Worst of all, I feel alone – terribly, terribly alone – and no wonder. Everybody's deserted me, because all I've done is scream and shout.

I snarl at Clive and the presenters.

I feel like thumping Forrester.

Even my Atlanteans experience the wrath of my psychosis.

I need to get out of here ... break out of this place. But my mind's in pieces – so shattered that I can't make a rational decision ... can't make sense of anything.

"Please, Duchess, you've got to eat. I'm breaking, and I can't help myself ... If this carries on, I don't know what's gonna happen. What am I gonna do? What am I gonna do?"

...

At last, Forrester's gone and the night's force-feeds are over. I need to get off this infernal stage and down into the kitchen ... get myself a cigarette and a strong cup of tea.

People ... lousy, rotten, conniving people! I hate them! *Hate them*!

None of this would have happened if it hadn't been for people sticking their oars in ...

That rotten sod Backhouse getting us kicked out of Hendle, then leaving Duchess and Herb'e to freeze in the back of an ice-cold van ...

Philip, sticking that bloody scalpel in me, then pressuring me to go to hospital ...

Clive, letting the fish company run rings around us ...

You couldn't make it up!

For months, I've been in the middle of a nightmare – a never-ending nightmare. I want help ... *need* help ... someone to guide me, because I just can't do this on my own anymore.

What's that? The back door of the dolphinarium has just slammed, yet it's gone eleven o'clock at night ... Who the hell can it be at this time?

I perceive a presence, a familiar presence – one I haven't experienced in a long, long time.

Why has my heart suddenly skipped a beat?

Someone's there ... standing in the shadows like a ghost, and, whoever he is, I sense that he's too afraid to step forward.

So who can it be? And why won't he move into the light?

...

Now, now I see him ... recognise the curve of his face. His features look strained, but he's still sporting that thick moustache above his lip.

Can it really be him?

He's aged ... aged a lot in the two years since we last met, and he looks somehow smaller.

I can't speak ... only stare. And it's more than obvious that he feels the same – scared that I might rebuff him.

My mouth's dry, and I swallow deeply.

"Gerry Mansell ... Is that really you?"

"Hello, David. Long time, no see."

Unbelievable! My old mentor, *actually* here at West Coast and standing less than eight feet away from me – the last person in the world I expected to see.

Open-mouthed, I shook my head in bewilderment, my mind still wrestling to take him in. Gerry's lips quivered nervously, before breaking into a sympathetic smile.

"I've only just heard about Herb'e, and, as I was in the neighbourhood, I wondered if you needed any help."

Well, he was spot on there, because if anyone needed assistance, I did.

"Thanks, Gerry – you don't know just how much that means to me ... I could really, *really* do with some support ... But what in the blazes are you doing here? The last I heard, you were working in Germany. How long have you been back in the UK?"

"Not long – a couple of weeks at most ... and, boy, am I *glad* to be here! There's nothing like the green, green grass of home to get your head straight."

That sounded ominous. Maybe there was more to Gerry's visit than at first met the eye.

"Pull up a chair while I put the kettle on. We've got a lot of catching up to do." A less than subtle nudge, but I was itching to know how life had been treating him.

"Yeah, like I said, it's a relief to be back on home turf. A foreign land can be a lonely place when you're in trouble – and I've been through the sort of experience I wouldn't wish on my worst enemy. Bleedin' dolphin shows – I'm up to 'ere with 'em!"

I sensed the abject bitterness in Gerry's tone, and it wasn't hard to guess what was coming next.

"I'm fed up to the back teeth of having to watch dolphins suffer … and even more fed up with having to watch them die."

"I know where you're coming from, Gerry. What a lousy business this *really* is. How many dolphins did you lose?"

"Virtually all of 'em – dolphins don't last long when they work in travelling shows. The tiny tanks and the stress of constant transports soon take their toll. If you get sixteen months out of 'em, you're lucky." Resignedly, he gave a shrug of his shoulders. "I don't suppose you've got a fag going spare, have you?"

Blimey, I'd thought I was the only one who bummed cigarettes … Even worse, I only had one left … Still …

"I've only ever had a brief glimpse of a travelling show, and that was when I was passing through City Zoo. The inflatable pool – if you could call it a pool – was so small that the dolphins could barely turn around. It was disgraceful – in fact, I don't know how they got away with it."

He drew deeply on his cigarette – *my* cigarette.

"Yeah … sounds pretty much like the outfit I was working for. Anyway, the crux of the matter is, I lost six dolphins in under eighteen months, so decided to walk. I just couldn't stand it anymore." He broke into a weak smile. "By the way, I've been speaking to Forrester, and he says that you worry too much. He reckons Herb'e will pull through."

Forrester? So the vet had been keeping my old teacher in the loop as to the goings-on at West Coast. Why was that? Why would an independent vet feed an ex-employee sensitive information about his old pool? Excuse the pun, but something smelt decidedly fishy.

"Well, Gerry, I don't care how many letters Forrester has after his name, he's got it wrong. Herb'e's dying – plain and simple – and there's nothing he or anyone else can do about it."

My old instructor knew better than to doubt me, because he'd witnessed the power of my *connection* too many times at the breaking pens of North Liston.

"I'm … I'm so sorry, David. I didn't realise it was that bad. After what Forrester told me, I just assumed … God! How long do you think Herb'e's got?"

I paused before answering. I thought I'd struggle to get my words out, but I'd become strangely calm – almost aloof.

"Four to five days at most – but, if I'm honest, my gut says sooner."

Through the dim light of the dungeon kitchen, I couldn't help but notice the signs of his agitation. The muscles in his cheeks were twitching, and his tongue roughed the ends of his moustache annoyingly. I suddenly became conscious that I was drifting away – a realisation that kick-started me into a change of subject.

"So, besides your world falling apart, what else is new?"

My quip was brazenly direct, but it at least helped to break the sticky atmosphere now pervading the room. Thus far, Gerry hadn't mentioned the scathing letter I'd received from his partner all that time ago – nevertheless, I could sense it was on his mind. So, out of courtesy, I decided to keep my mouth shut and protect our fragile truce.

What a bizarre twist of fate: two broken trainers – once recognised as Europe's finest – drowning their sorrows in one last musing. I shivered …

… my career had gone full circle – it had begun with Gerry, and it would end with Gerry.

For me, Gerry's return was nothing short of heaven-sent, so why were my alarm bells ringing so loudly? After all, I'd been granted at least a part of the miracle I'd been praying for. Nevertheless, I couldn't shake the feeling that things were not what they seemed, that my old instructor had not just happened to be in the neighbourhood as he'd claimed, but rather that he was here for a specific reason. Still, in my present distraught state, I'd be the last one to look a gift horse in the mouth. I desperately needed help, and there was none better qualified than Gerry to give it.

The following day, after completing the morning force-feeds, Forrester coolly informed me that he'd revised his previous assessment of Herb'e's condition, so had followed procedure by reporting the situation to Rogers at City Head Office. He also said that he would be camped at West Coast until further notice. In other words, he'd finally accepted my prognosis.

On hearing this, the West Coast Management immediately issued orders to disband my one-time super team by pairing Duchess with Scouse – a move that, no matter how painful, I knew to be proper. After all, we were still in high season, and the paying public would be well within their rights to expect a two-dolphin show. Nevertheless, the enforced break-up of my *Perfect Pair* would be a bitter pill to swallow – the final nail in the coffin of what had once been Europe's greatest performers.

Resigned, I had no option but to comply with Company demands. Herb'e was already lost to me, but Duchess still had a fighting chance of survival. She had stayed by her partner's side, loyally embracing his mind-set by not accepting fish – a sacrifice I couldn't allow to continue. So, come what may, tomorrow morning, I would officially break my team.

I'd clung onto my dream for long enough – it was time to part my *Perfect Pair* forever.

❦ 135 ❧

"David, I need you to prepare Herb'e now for the morning force-feed. That way you'll have more time to get ready for your afternoon shows."

Oh, that's big of him! Forrester acts like he's doing me a favour. I mean, Herb'e might be dying, but we can't disappoint the precious public, can we? Especially not while there's a shedload of money still to be made … No, that would never do … The show *must* go on!

This whole, rotten set-up makes me want to puke – Forrester in particular … I mean, why *do* we have to put Herb'e through this torture? For God's sake, what's it gonna achieve?

"Tony, do you mind telling me why we're even doing this? Herb'e's dying, and no matter how much fish you stuff down him, that's not gonna change. He needs to be left in peace, not tormented like this …"

I feel Gerry's hand on my shoulder – he's trying to calm me down. Well, it's not bloody working, because I know that what we're doing is wrong, totally wrong.

"Look, David, I know you're upset, but we can't just give in. Remember, Tony's the vet, so he knows best."

Like hell, he does!

Gerry's supposed to be supporting me, not sucking up to some rotten vet. Anyway, who does he think he is, waltzing in here and giving orders? Duchess and Herb'e are *my* dolphins, not his, and this isn't *his* pool anymore – it's mine. How dare he? How dare …

"*Bullshit*, Gerry! This is all bullshit! We need to afford Herb'e some dignity … need to let him go. Why can't either of you see that? What the hell's wrong with you both?"

...

Finally! We're finished! Thank God! The end of yet another pointless force-feed.

I've barely had time to get Herb'e off the false floor and Management's already screaming for the start of the first show – a performance they want me to do with Duchess and Scouse ...

Christ! What's wrong with everybody in this rotten place?

Duchess has barely started taking fish, yet they're pushing her to perform. For crying out loud, am I the only sane Joe around here?

Well, stuff 'em! Stuff the lot of 'em! They can all go to hell for me, because I'm not doing it!

How can they expect me to stand on stage and work Duchess without *him*? How can I look at her and not see Herb'e by her side?

I can't ... I just can't ... my mind won't take it ... Whatever I thought yesterday, I cannot bring myself to break my team ... It's a one-dolphin show with Scouse or no show at all ...

I hate them ... hate the men in suits ...

... but worst of all ... I hate myself.

My world is collapsing around me, and all I want to do is lash out ...

"Come on, Capello – get a grip!"

Gerry's just pulled me a chair, beckoned me to sit down. But what does *he* know? What does anyone know?

"Listen to me, David, just listen to me! You're losing it big-time! You've got to get a hold ... especially now, because I've got something to tell you – something very important – so I need you to listen ... listen good!"

He's pinned my arms to my sides in an effort to subdue me – for his sake, he'd better not let go.

"Now, listen up, David ... I've recently been working with a reporter from a major Sunday newspaper – a journalist who wants to write an exposé on dolphinariums. He wants me to spill the beans on the captive dolphin industry – tell the public the truth about what goes on behind closed doors."

"You'd better not let go of me, Mansell ... I mean it ... you'd better not let go! Anyway, what the hell has all this got to do with me? What do I care about you or your bloody story?"

I flash him my teeth, and his grip weakens.

"Please, just let me finish – hear me out! The headline is going to be *Suicide Dolphins*, and I *need* you to back me up. Think … think back to North Liston … what happened to Bubbles … how she topped herself rather than spend the rest of her days in captivity …"

Topped herself? Topped herself? But did she? Can I trust him? Or is he just playing with words to get me onside?

"Then there's the force-feeds … all those horrific force-feeds … Just think how outraged the public would be if they knew about them. They'd go bonkers – never set foot in a dolphinarium again. Think, David … think what the two of us could achieve if we stood together. We could blow this lousy, rotten, bleedin' industry to smithereens. No one would dare argue with Europe's top trainers. Come on, David, come on! You know it makes sense! I've got us the window, *so* let's use it!"

Gerry's grip has slackened to such an extent that I could easily break free – if I wanted to … *if* I wanted to.

"No matter how much you love your dolphins, David, it's too late for them. But we can make damn sure that this doesn't happen to any other dolphins. We can stop the UK dolphinarium industry in its tracks. *You* can make a difference, David … *We* can make a difference – together, we'd be invincible."

I need to catch my breath. My head is still reeling, but that red mist is fading.

"Okay, Gerry. First, take your hands off me or we're gonna have trouble. Once you've done that, we can talk."

He's anxious – doesn't know how I'll react – but he needn't worry. I know he's right: the only way I can help my friends is by finally facing up to the truth.

Feel sick – like I want to throw up – but, most of all, I *feel* angry.

"Right, Gerry, you're the boss. It's your contact, so it's your call. Let's screw the lousy bastards … let's screw 'em good!"

So much for Gerry being in the neighbourhood – now I know the *real* reason why he came back.

clyde rules

❧ 136 ❧

Clamouring crowds finally gone, not even their echo remains.

Sad of eye, I stand alone with my thoughts, resignedly dissecting the evening mist rolling across the mirror's face.

Silence broken only by the gentle notes of lapping water – a haunting overture intermittently accompanied by the symphonic eruptions of pushed air.

A wistful smile lifts my features: the sight of three slumbering dolphins, my beloved charges wrapped in a shawl of liquid lace.

I never tire of their rhythmic dance, that flawless weave born of ocean magic.

Mere words cannot describe the magnificence of these extraordinary beings – a sea god's masterpiece conceived at the beginning of time.

Sleek forms moulded in the furnace of a bubbling broth; proud citizens of Atlantis meticulously sculpted by Neptune's own hand.

My beautiful, beautiful people …

Deep in thought, I cannot help but wonder: will they ever find peace with humankind? Or will they be forever condemned to bear the mask of a circus clown?

Dolphinariums … dolphinariums …

… rotten, bloody dolphinariums!

❦ 137 ❧

Damp, claustrophobic and unforgiving – the *Waiting Room*.

Waiting, waiting …

… drinking lukewarm tea and waiting for Herb'e's last farewell.

Waiting, waiting …

… staring at a blank wall and waiting for the inevitable Management reprimand for my insubordination.

Waiting, waiting …

… smoking cigarettes and waiting for Gerry's reporter friend to make his grand entrance.

Waiting, waiting …

… "eating" cigarettes and waiting for the vet to arrive.

Waiting, waiting … always waiting …

As I gazed around, I couldn't help but notice a marked acceleration in the spread of the spidery brushstrokes that framed the kitchen wall, stirring my imagination to paint pictures across the bleak canvas within.

I could plainly see the rolling storm clouds burrowing into an angry sea; a vast, swirling maelstrom effortlessly smashed asunder by the huge bulk of a lone sea-giant – a great whale going head-to-head with a ferocious ocean. Quite literally the Clash of the Titans.

The vision seemed so real that I could actually *feel* the sting of salt needles as the great beast swung himself around to meet the oncoming wave, the tsunami exploding to thrust a myriad micro-organisms against his baleen plates.

I vigorously sieved my tea through bared teeth.

Reaching to free yet another cigarette, I couldn't help but muse as to how many times I'd found myself sitting alone in the confines of this dungeon kitchen. What a depressing place – there was barely enough room to swing a cat … meaning it was time for me to leave. No more smokes for me tonight – well, not in this hellhole, anyway. One final check on my charges and I'd be gone.

Then it happened: as I stepped onto the stage, I sensed a defining change – something I couldn't immediately identify – a numbing melancholy that courted an overwhelming feeling of emptiness. My eyes instinctively flashed to Duchess, who was schooling alongside Scouse … leaving Herb'e to swim alone.

Cocking my head to scan the airwaves, I detected no semblance of a *connection* – just a nothingness.

Could it be that Duchess had finally accepted that she was going to lose Herb'e? Or was this something more?

Something more … I had the strangest feeling that this was no longer about Herb'e alone – it was also about me. Had my princess suddenly realised that the magic of her spell was waning? That she'd never been closer to losing her chosen prince?

There was no denying that my once-receptive mind had buckled under the relentless pressure of the last twelve months, degrading our spiritual bond into nothing more than a meaningless mishmash of sound.

Nevertheless, it wasn't so far gone as not to perceive that it had lost something irreplaceable. In the pool, I saw three dolphins swimming, yet my third eye registered only two, which meant that, at some point during the last thirty minutes, something catastrophic had taken place … I had lost a friend.

Closing my eyes tightly, I scanned the darkness for my missing Atlantean, but sensed only a spotlight dimming on an empty stage. Then, through the ether, I heard the roar of a crowd baying for more, along with the resonant voice of an unknown compère. With typical showbiz razzmatazz:

"Ladies and gentlemen, boys and girls, Flippa has left the building …"

So, this was it – my ultimate test was upon me, and I needed none of my much-vaunted psychic ability to prepare myself for what was coming next.

It had been less than five days since I'd shocked Gerry with my revelation about Herb'e – a chilling end-of-days prediction. The mischievous Atlantean who had for so long shared my life was now well and truly gone, having made good his escape at least two hours earlier. Unfortunately, a luxury that would not extend to me, meaning I would now be forced to bear witness to the final throes of the empty vessel that had once been my friend – an experience that would be nothing short of traumatic and would haunt me for the rest of my days.

Even so, life, as they say, goes on, borne out by the early morning visit of the fastidious vet. By 6.45 am, Forrester was already preparing for yet more pointless injections and force-feeds, treatments he knew I fiercely opposed. However, in my present distraught state, my once-valued opinion counted for little, which left the scientists an open-field to have their way.

All was now lost. I felt usurped within the confines of my own pool, and the relentless loss of sleep had stolen any fight I had left. To all intents and purposes, I was a clone of Herb'e's empty husk, falling zombie-like into an inescapable fog.

However, even in the depths of my despair, I found it impossible not to be distressed by the behaviour of Duchess and Scouse. Throughout this entire living nightmare, both my Atlanteans had continued to school together, choosing to leave Herb'e's failing shell to flounder alone.

Yet why was I so appalled? After all, I'd viewed this behaviour many times when death had come calling. In fact, I'd trained myself to accept it – even embrace it. So why should I again find myself questioning it?

The sad truth was that no matter how fondly I held these exceptional people, I still found it impossible to accept their ethos. The manufactured morals of my human conditioning would always stand in my way.

This intolerance was a handicap that would always leave me on the outside looking in. A curse that would find me forever torn between two contrasting beliefs, thus branding me an anomaly – a being mentally touched by both human and Atlantean concepts … and in grave peril of being accepted by neither.

❦ 139 ❧

Logbook entry 13th August 1974, 9.30 am: Herb'e injected with gentamicin before force-feeding vitamin-loaded fish and eight Lomotil tablets. Note: Herb'e has started discharging heavy waste (black in colour).

Although still relatively early, the dolphinarium had quickly sprung into life, Fun City security guards swelling the ranks of my grey-faced staff. The atmosphere took on a surreal feel as the hushed crowd lingered aimlessly around the pool's safety barriers. No one dared speak. Even my presenters refrained from pressing me about the afternoon show rotas – performances I prayed that Management would cut.

"David, I'm sorry for not getting here sooner, but I've literally just come off the 'phone to City Head Office."

At last, the elusive Clive Rothwell had seen fit to brave a visit.

"I've informed Mr Rogers just how bad the situation is with Herb'e and told him that I'm officially cancelling all of today's shows. I've made it clear that it would be highly inappropriate to expect either you or any member of your team to go on stage under the present circumstances."

Clive's sympathetic response again reminded me that not *all* managers had hearts of stone – scrapping a full day's performances during peak season was a bold call that wouldn't make him popular.

"As you can imagine, the cancellations haven't gone down well with Mr Rogers, so ... so ... Look, David, you're not going to like this, but Mr Rogers has insisted that Mr Backhouse come down here to monitor the situation."

I couldn't help but respond with a cynical laugh – Backhouse, Rogers' golden boy, actually *here* at West Coast.

"Well, Clive, in view of my chequered history with Backhouse, that's just the sort of lunatic decision I *would* expect from City Head Office. I will always hold that conniving bastard personally responsible for what's happening here, so you can get straight back on to Rogers and tell him just how *grateful* we all are that his pet rat is even honouring us with his presence. I mean, how did we ever cope without him?"

I might be on the verge of losing my mind, but I certainly hadn't lost my cynicism.

Clive gave me the sort of sheepish smirk that told me he wanted Backhouse here no more than I did. Still, Rogers – in his infinite wisdom - had made his decision, meaning we mere underlings would have to accept it.

Logbook entry 13th August 1974, 12 noon: The condition of Herb'e has greatly worsened. The ejection of heavy, black waste is now constant.

Later that afternoon, a dishevelled Gerry stumbled into the dolphinarium.

"God, it's all right for some – what time do you call this? Blimey, Gerry, you look like I feel. How many did you knock back last night?"

Although Gerry was plainly suffering from a serious hangover, he wore a crestfallen expression that signalled something more.

"Aargh! Don't even go there! Anyway, how's Herb'e?"

A stupid question if ever I'd heard one – and further confirmation that Gerry had something else on his mind. He didn't even wait for my reply.

"I've had some bad news, David ... some very bad news."

Bad news? Well, there's a surprise ... What now?

140

"If you're waiting for that lousy reporter to arrive, David, you can forget it, because he's *not* coming. I spoke to him last night, and he told me that his editor has ordered him to drop the story and walk away. In other words … bury it!"

The tone of Gerry's voice made it clear that he was not just devastated, but also enraged. Understandable, as he'd pinned all his hopes on getting this exposé out. However, for me, this news had little meaning, as my mind was now closed to everything except my stricken Atlantean. I answered dully.

"Sounds like someone got to his editor, Gerry – someone influential, because I would imagine it takes an awful lot of clout to intimidate a major newspaper."

"I'll say," Gerry snapped, "my contact was distraught, especially after all the work he'd put in. I actually heard him pleading with his boss on the 'phone, but he wasn't having any of it – just repeated his order to dump the story and not look back. The lousy bastard!" Gerry instinctively lowered his voice. "You know, David, this smacks of the Old Boys' Network in all its glory. I don't know why I'm so surprised – there's just too much money invested in dolphinariums to allow anyone to rock the boat."

The Old Boys' Network … I'd heard mention of this before – a controlling hierarchy that pulled the strings of big business. A truly fascinating concept.

"You see, David, it's like they're untouchable. You can't pin the rotten sods down, because they never put anything in writing. Everything is done by word-of-mouth – in most cases, over the 'phone. Try to imagine the biggest conglomerate you know — and I do mean *big* — a household name that goes on to breed lots of totally unrelated subsidiaries. Companies that, in turn, spawn even more subsidiaries, until they create a kind of super pyramid. A shit heap where the squeaky-clean corporate daddy sits at the top, far removed from the dubious business ventures that would give it a bad name — in our case, dolphinariums.

"What's even more sickening is that these companies are run by the pride of the British aristocracy — the oh-so-respectable and untouchable Lord and Lady Muck …"

What an outburst! No wonder Gerry was ticked-off — yet he'd only voiced what I'd long-suspected about the financing of the UK and European dolphinariums … with one *word* in particular leaping from his rant — the word "untouchable". A quality that, in future years, would come back to haunt me.

Logbook entry 13th August 1974, 4.30 pm: Injected Herb'e with more gentamicin, then force-fed three and a half pounds of fresh herring … His condition is visibly worsening.

"David, I know you don't agree with these force-feeds, but you've got to try and understand Forrester's dilemma. He works on facts, not feelings, so he's just doing what the …"

Gerry's voice cut short, his torso abruptly cranking straight. His only other movement was the slow clenching of a fist … Even so it was impossible not to *feel* the fire in his vision as it lasered into the shadows behind me. Taking a deep breath, I slowly turned around to face the lone figure that was now standing on the concrete walkway …

… Backhouse!

141

Backhouse remained frozen in the shadows at the far side of the pool. From where I was standing, it was practically impossible to read his expression, but there was no mistaking that pale oval face ghosting through the darkness – or his unease as he focussed on the last person in the world he expected to see … Gerry!

Clearly, the sight of my old mentor had thrown him into a panic – not surprising, as Gerry would still be Company head trainer had it not been for Backhouse's underhand shenanigans; *not* the first time that my general manager had intentionally sabotaged Gerry's career. If the dolphin grapevine were to be believed, it had happened once before when they'd worked together at a major dolphinarium in the south.

Either way, Backhouse would have to tread carefully. He was no longer safely ensconced at my beloved Hendle; he was at a hostile West Coast and facing two men who loathed him … two men with very little to lose.

"Ah, there you are, Mr Backhouse … Sorry to have kept you waiting, but I had a pressing problem with one of the Fun City attractions. I do apologise."

As he turned briskly to Clive, Backhouse's relief was palpable. It seemed that the golden boy of the dolphin project was well outside his comfort zone and, what's more, everyone knew it – including Clive …, which immediately got me thinking. Had Clive *really* been delayed? Or had he purposely left Backhouse to stew in the lion's den? I strongly suspected the latter.

Logbook entry 13th August 1974, 11.00 pm: Herb'e injected with gentamicin and B12. Herb'e is now swimming badly, listing and banging into the sides of the pool walls, which means his sonar is failing.

Their images and egos fade … far, far away, banished to another space in time by a mind still struggling to make sense of it all. Backhouse and Gerry, forcefully pushed aside by a psyche steeling itself for the inevitable. And so it had begun. The moment of truth would soon be upon me.

Logbook entry 13th August 1974, midnight: Herb'e's swimming has further deteriorated, and he's now listing badly … sonar getting worse.

Quietly and meticulously, I placed my snorkel, facemask and flippers at the edge of the stage. My work topside was now at an end, and the next few hours would see me constantly in the water. The horror I'd been dreading would soon come to pass. The endgame had begun …

… and begun in earnest.

142

I suppose I should be grateful that Duchess has started eating again. After all, by joining Herb'e in his mind-set, she's more than done her duty …

But I'm not.

I should be happy that she's no longer refusing food … that she's found the strength to move on with her life …

But I'm not.

She's eaten a hearty meal, and now she's swimming in the direction of Scouse – already in search of a new mate, checking out Herb'e's replacement.

Poor Scouse! He has no idea of the powerful *domina* coming his way. Duchess … my beautiful, beautiful …

How *could* she do that? How *could* she desert Herb'e? Leave him to die alone? *How?*

I'm so tired that my mind is blurring, and it's affecting my judgment. This *is* the dolphin way. I've seen it many times before, so why am I going back over it again? After all, it's survival – survival of the fittest. I know this. I've always known this … but, still, I didn't expect it of *her!* Not my princess … How *could* she do this to him? *How?*

Nothing makes sense anymore …

It's the early hours of the morning, and the dolphinarium has taken on a sinister silence, yet there are still plenty of people milling around. But they won't look at me. All they do is huddle together and whisper – whisper in corners. Well, let them! What do I care what they're saying? People … I hate them! All of them!

Sounds – dull sounds – the laboured snorts from Herb'e's blowhole as he struggles for breath … Or is it life? I'm not sure. What's wrong with me? My mind has gone into a stall. It's not computing anymore. I'm at Hell's gates, and I can't walk away.

Got to get it together, because I can't delay any longer. My friend's in trouble: Herb'e's no longer weaving the water – he's struggling to maintain his buoyancy, and there's no one but me who can help him. I'm going to have to get into the pool … use my body as a prop … piggyback him to keep his head above water or he'll drown.

Whatever happens, I daren't tire. I've got to stay strong for him … remind myself that *nobody* – but *nobody* – is better in the water than I am …

Can't let Herb'e down … not again.

I'm biting so hard on the mouthpiece of my snorkel that I'm shutting off the airway. How did it come to this? How did something so beautiful turn so ugly?

Swimming, swimming … my head's swimming … floundering in a watery haze …

Herb'e, *my* Herb'e … But this *isn't my* Herb'e anymore. This is nothing more than his discarded shell, because *my* Herb'e has already gone … already made good his escape …

…

So tired … so sleepy … I've been cradling Herb'e through vomit-filled water for nearly an hour and a half and – incredibly – the pain that was racking my body has faded, lulling my senses into sleep. That's a bad sign … I need to leave the pool, work my cramped muscles back to life …

… but not yet, not yet … I can't leave him yet.

It's strange – never noticed it before – but from the waterline, the chatter of the people standing topside sounds like a lullaby of jumbled words – a confused cacophony of noise echoing down through an invisible ceiling into an eerie void. Muffled voices reverberating, merging – the sound of people … people … people …

Aargh! Pain … excruciating cramp in my leg. Got to get out of the water fast – get one of the presenters to give me a five-minute rub-down …

Would you believe it? The hard-faced bastard! Backhouse, bold as brass, standing on the stage and talking to Forrester – only five yards from where I've just hauled myself out.

I'm surprised he's found the guts to get so close, especially after the last time we faced each other off. I can still see him, wet and bedraggled … and standing perilously close to the edge of that empty Hendle pool. What a missed opportunity that was! Thirteen feet would have been a long way to fall … an awful long way.

He's clocked my gaze, so averted his eyes – a wise move.

"Hey, do you lot think I'm sitting here for the good of my health or what?"

The very sight of Backhouse has got me shouting again, and that's not me – never has been me. But, just lately, I can't seem to help myself. It's this rotten, lousy job – it's turned me into someone I hardly recognise.

"Sorry, David, I'm so tired and upset that I didn't think. Now, where does it hurt?"

The answer to her question is "everywhere", but best I keep my mouth shut, because she's just a young presenter and none of this is her fault … It's *his*.

If Backhouse hadn't left Herb'e in the back of that freezing-cold van, none of this would be happening. Still, it's no good torturing myself, because, right now, I've got enough on my plate. Besides, the air temperature inside the dolphinarium has plummeted, and I'm beginning to feel the cold. I'm even starting to shiver, which means I need to get back into the warmth of the water.

The cold air has caused a grey carpet-mist to hang over the arena like a shroud, veiling Herb'e's struggle to stay afloat. Even so, I can still see his dorsal fin cutting a trail through the watery haze.

It's a weird feeling slipping through the mist – like falling through a raincloud into a balmy liquid sky, a comforting reminder that I'm back in my element. Only need to adjust my facemask and clear my snorkel, then I'll be ready … ready to start again.

There … job done! Now then … Where's Herb'e …? *Where's Herb'e?*

He was here a second ago … on my right. Must have spun around clearing my mask – lost my bearings – which means he must be on my left … But he's not … He's not there … Herb'e's *not there*!

I know I'm disoriented, but if he's not on my left and he's not on my right, he's *got* to be behind me … But he's not … He's *not there, either!*

So where the heck is he? *Where's* he gone?

In my panic, I've just swallowed half the rotten pool, and I really need to pause and clear my throat, but there isn't time … I've got to find him … Where is he? *Where is he?*

Can't see him … Can't see him anywhere …

Oh, God! Oh, God! He *must* have gone under … Got to dive … got to find him … Come on, Capello, he can't be more than a few feet away! Use your eyes, man! Look … *look!*

I see him – he's below me … *sinking* … sinking tail-first like a lead weight …

God! God! Got to get to him … got to catch him, but can't seem to reach him. Come on, Capello, kick those legs! Herb'e needs you … You *have* to get hold of him.

What's wrong with me? What the hell's *wrong* with me? Nobody's stronger in the water than I am, so why can't I get to him? Why?

Falling … falling … Herb'e's falling down a vortex, and I'm dropping after him … But he's *still* out of reach …

His face … I see *his* face … He's smiling at me, actually smiling … How can he be *smiling*?

Time has slowed to a crawl, and the vortex is growing deeper. Move it, Capello! For pity's sake, *move it*!

My co-ordination is gone – totally wrecked – and my arms and legs are flailing … I'm swimming like a frog.

His smile – Herb'e's smile – it's changed. He's not smiling anymore … he's *grinning*.

What the …? What's this? Been hit by a cloud – a dirty, horrible, green cloud, so thick I can hardly see. What's happening? *What's going on?*

Oh, no! Herb'e's bowels must have opened. I'm actually clawing my way through faeces … His waste is sticking to my body like tiny leeches …

Can't let that stop me … Got to get to him … get to him *now* …

Nearly there – just a few more feet, and I'll have him. He's landed, landed tail-first, but he's going into a slow-motion fall, like a felled tree. Daren't let him end up flat on the pool floor, or I'll never be able to budge him.

Have to get hold of him … and quick …!

…

GOT HIM!

Heaven knows how, but I've managed to wedge my knee under his body and prop him up – but he weighs a ton and I don't know how long I can hold him. Have to stay focussed! Can't let blind panic get the better of me … Somehow, I've …

… I've …

… I've …

Suddenly gone quiet. No sound anymore. No garbled shrieks from above. Just silence – a dead, almost soothing hush. Again, I seem to be standing outside time. It's surreal – my heartbeat has slowed, and that inner turmoil has given way to a measured calm. What's more, my viewpoint has changed: I see two figures inside a water bubble – a boy squatting on a pool floor, nursing a stricken Atlantean. They strike a statuesque pose – two embracing lovers trapped within a snow globe.

But the statue isn't quite finished – it requires adjustment – so I summon the puppetmaster to complete the work …

My psyche meticulously rearranges the boy's legs, positioning them to give him maximum upward thrust. Next, it rotates the fallen Atlantean from side to belly to allow the boy to get a firmer grip on his pectoral fins.

Are the two figures in the correct position? Are they balanced? I can't afford to get this wrong, or the boy's endeavour will fail.

I inhale.

They're ready.

They're a full thirteen feet below the waterline, so the boy will need all his strength to springboard his friend up towards the light. One word – just one simple word – will break the spell that holds back time …

Push!

Muted shouts, muffled screams – an echo of panic shatters the time barrier … But that won't stop me … Nothing will stop me … We're hurtling upwards … spearing through clouds of faeces and vomit …

Air … the smash of cold, fresh air as we explode into the frenzy.

Aargh! My ears! My ears!

I've hit a wall of excruciating sound – shouting, screaming … It's horrible!

"Quick! Don't just stand there! Get the stretcher into the water! We need to get Herb'e out!"

Hear Forrester barking orders ... Confusion ... Pandemonium ... It's all happening so fast – yet, instinctively, I've managed to get Herb'e alongside and harnessed in record time.

More frantic cries! I can't stand it anymore! Got to get my head back under the water ... kill the volume ...

Seconds ... submerged for mere seconds. A lifetime.

Herb'e's disappeared ... already torn away forever by a bunch of well-meaning strangers and self-professed dolphin experts. But what's worse – what really sticks in the craw – is that one of them is Backhouse.

Little wonder he still won't look at me, because he certainly has a lot to answer for. Had it not been for his relentless jealousy, this nightmare would never have happened.

"He's gone ... Herb'e's gone ..."

Forrester ... I'll never forget those words: "He's gone ... Herb'e's gone ..." Just four quietly-spoken words to bring down the curtain on the greatest Flippa dolphin of them all – and a beloved friend.

Since I left the water, no one's spoken to me. In fact, I'm not sure they're aware I'm even here. It's as if I've suddenly become invisible ...

Invisible ... maybe I am.

Maybe now is the time to slip away and start anew. After all, what have I got to look forward to here? Nothing – except further heartache at the hands of Backhouse and his glove-puppet Rogers.

Yeah, maybe this is the time to make *my* escape. After all, the cell door is open – open wide.

The question is: have I the courage to walk through it?

143

Filled with morbid curiosity, the vultures formed an impenetrable wall around Herb'e's lifeless body. Not surprising, as it wasn't every day they got the chance to be up-close and personal with such an esteemed Atlantean. In fact, they were so preoccupied that they didn't even notice me as I walked from the stage and down to the kitchen. After all, what entertainment could there possibly be in the pathetic sight of a broken trainer?

As I leaned on the table, head-in-hands, the stink of Herb'e's waste hit me. I desperately needed a shower, yet all I wanted to do was pack a bag and run as far away as possible. But, even in my despair, my obsessive nature demanded one final task – the closing entry into Herb'e's diary.

> *Logbook entry 14th August 1974, 2.30 am: Flippa began to struggle badly to stay afloat. I swam him around the pool for some time. There was continuous vomiting until he went into shock. Then he died.*
>
> *Post-mortem due to be carried out by attending vet, Tony Forrester.*
> *The End.*
> *Signed: Trainer, David Capello.*

My last account – described with cold efficiency and totally devoid of emotion.

Placing my pen alongside my empty pack of cigarettes, I couldn't help but wonder … Would anyone ever read these logbooks … ever read about this remarkable Atlantean? Or would the Company eradicate his memory at the earliest opportunity?

Who knew?

Who cared?

I cared.

I struggled to recall the good times that Herb'e and I had shared – but, if truth be known, since our arrival at West Coast, there had been precious few. That fateful day at Hendle had put paid to them.

Backhouse … Tommy Backhouse … At this moment in time, I should have been upstairs tearing his head off. After all, it was no less than he deserved. Yet, ironically, nothing was further from my mind, because – strange as it seemed – he had ceased to matter. My hatred for my general manager, along with my reluctant respect for Forrester, had totally dissipated. Even my admiration for Gerry had gone – wiped clean by a shattered psyche.

But how could this be? For better or for worse, these three men had played an integral role in my life as a trainer, yet my mind now deemed them nonentities.

Without doubt, my underwater ordeal with my dying friend had taken its toll, leaving me blank – as blank as the kitchen wall that had so often transfixed me.

Determinedly, I grabbed my battered holdall and took one last glance at the kitchen table – just an empty fag packet, a pen and Herb'e's diaries …

… seven battered books cataloguing the extraordinary story of his life in captivity …

… *his* life in captivity …

… *our* life in captivity …

… *my* life in captivity.

144

Door forever closed on my dungeon kitchen, I stand motionless within the shadow of the arena.

Wrapped in a cloak of invisibility, I remain masked to all but Gerry.

Though our eyes meet, no words are spoken …

Yes, we have an understanding, he and I.

He's transfixed as I allow him to relive the horrors of a foreign land through the eyes of his protégé.

Death wears no badge of nationality, for it is universal …

Yes, we have an understanding, he and I.

He knows I am about to follow in his footsteps, turning my back on what had once been my dream … *His* dream …

Yes, we have an understanding, he and I.

He knows I will soon disappear, as does *she* – my love, my life, my beautiful, beautiful Duchess.

I promised I would never leave, always stay by her side.

But that was a billion heartbeats ago …

… a promise made by one who still viewed the world through innocent eyes …

… a promise that will be broken by the opening of a door.

Duchess – my poor, beautiful Duchess.

Will she ever forgive me?

Will I ever forgive myself?

Or will her vision torture me for the rest of my days?

Who knows?

The Fates know … for this is their game.

Duchess – my poor, beautiful Duchess.

Only Gerry sees me slip away …

Yes, we have an understanding, he and I.

He always maintained how very much alike we were.

Such a pity that we shall never meet again …

…

Yes, we *had* an understanding, he and I.

❦ 145 ❧

The driving rain pelted the windscreen, blurring the flashes of orange fire lining the deserted motorway – a sheeting wall of water that danced to the rhythm of the wiper blades. Despite the dire conditions, my foot remained firmly on the pedal. I was fleeing, desperate to escape the curse of West Coast.

I was already finding the events of the last twenty-four hours difficult to recall – experiencing gaps in my memory, as if my subconscious were transferring much of the heartache to a darkened room … a room without a view. Nevertheless, I remained filled with guilt.

How would I live with myself? How would I ever be able to look in a mirror and *not* see her face – the girl I'd left behind … Duchess?

They say that a man should never cry; that tears are a sign of weakness. But *this* man did cry – he cried all the way home, so hard that he could barely navigate the winding roads leading from the motorway.

What a pathetic sight I must have looked to Mum when she opened the door: swollen eyes, unshaven face and long, salt-matted hair – to say nothing of the stink of faeces dried to a clay by the heat of my car.

She looked at me appalled. "Oh, David! What's on earth's happened?"

My stiff upper lip crumbled, loosing yet another torrent of tears.

"He's dead, Mum … Herb'e's dead … and I don't know what to do …"

Mum gathered me into her arms and hugged me for several moments before gently guiding me into the house.

"Right, my lad – first job is to get you looking presentable, so let's get you out of those rotten, filthy clothes and into a hot bath. When you're washed and dressed, I'll put the kettle on, and you can tell me exactly what's happened."

I couldn't help but smile – I was a kid again, when a hot bath and a cup of tea were the answer to all my woes. Thankfully, some things never changed.

Some things never changed ... But, of course, some things did: *I* had changed – changed a lot. Over time, my Atlanteans had honed my mental capabilities to an exceptional level, meaning that my mind would now demand – and get – retribution for Herb'e's death.

I clearly remembered that incident at Hendle with Duchess and the scalpel; how Duchess had dragged my psyche into that forbidden room, sparking an inner-evolution – the acquisition of a singular ability that I could invoke in times of great stress.

I sensed the coming of a fury, and those who doubted the power of my mind would be in for a rude awakening, one that would change their perception of me forever ...

... one that they would never forget.

❦ 146 ❧

Finally, the darkness has driven away the light. I was beginning to think that this horrible day would never end. I need to rest my tortured mind … shut out the world. Sleep.

...

My eyes have barely closed, yet I'm aware of my arms flailing – I'm falling headlong through murky shadows … down, down, down into black waters.

Within the liquid chromite, I see faces – a montage of grotesque, twisted faces. Drowned souls from the Id – some laughing, some leering, all pointing … aiming the finger of accusation. Their hideous cackle is tearing through the void.

"Why couldn't you reach him, Capello?"

"You're *supposed* to be a hot-shot trainer – an expert in the water. So why did you swim like a frog?"

"What was your problem? Did you even *want* to save him?"

His face … I see Herb'e's grinning face. His death mask.

Drowning … drowning … being sucked down a vortex and desperately need someone to get me out. But nobody's helping … They're just standing and staring …What's wrong with them? Why won't they help? Why won't …

...

Am I swimming, or am I floating? I'm not sure, because I can't feel anything. All I know is that I'm looking down – down from high above the West Coast arena.

I'm aware of dolphin snorts echoing through the silence, yet no sound reaches my ears. From this elevated perch, I can clearly see Duchess schooling alongside Scouse, their sleek bodies trailing soft patterns across the water … But there's no trace of …

A scream rips through my head …

… I'm in a new location – the stage.

She's awake … she knows I'm here.

"How could you leave him to die alone, Duchess? Why did you desert him when he needed you?"

She's trying to answer – trying to get through – but the thunder in my head drowns her out. I'm not interested in her excuses – all I want to do is lash out.

That ornamental netting hanging from the wall, the brightly-painted boat and the multi-coloured rings … When I come to think of just how long I spent decorating this stage, it makes my blood boil. All that hard work – and for what? A money-grabbing, back-stabbing Company that couldn't give a toss about anyone or anything. Well, sod 'em! Sod the lot of them! They're nothing but a load of suited parasites.

"Please, David, try to stay calm … You need to listen to me."

Did she actually say "stay calm"? She must be joking – especially after what *she* did. I've had it up to here with everyone, including *her*. It's about time I gave them all a taste of their own medicine – showed them how much damage I can *really* do … starting with that netting display … *my* netting display. And I'm not gonna stop there. There's the props too … *my* props. Yeah, if the men in suits want them, they can damn well get in the pool and fish 'em out.

Footsteps – *people!*

People coming, which means I'm gonna have to cut it short and get out of here fast!

…

Whoa! What a dream! So vivid, it felt as if I were really there, tearing up the West Coast stage; so real, I'm actually experiencing disorientation.

Wha …? What's that ringing? Sounds like the telephone …

It *is* the telephone – but who could be calling at this unearthly hour? It's the early hours of the morning, for God's sake!

Mum's just raced past my room – blimey, she's quick!

She's speaking, but in a whisper. Obviously, she's trying not to wake us all up. Well, I hope she gives whoever it is a piece of her mind, because they've certainly got a nerve ringing at this time. Normally, I'd get up and find out who it is, but I can't … I'm absolutely shattered … feel like I've just gone ten rounds with Muhammad Ali …

Need to sleep …

Tomorrow … I'll ask her about the 'phone call tomorrow.

147

A piping hot teapot strategically placed in the centre of the breakfast table beside a plate of buttered crumpets and thick, jammy toast. A breakfast fit for a king – and all lovingly prepared by Mum. Yet I couldn't eat a bite.

"The cheek of him – demanding to speak to you at that time. As if they haven't put you through enough … I mean, look of the state of you – you've cried so hard that your face looks like a football. Anyway, I gave your manager a piece of my mind."

I bet she did – although Mum was always polite, she didn't wrap things up.

"'Mr Rothwell,' I said, 'first, I don't appreciate being wakened at five in the morning. Second, I have no intention of bringing David to the telephone, especially in his state. I don't know what you did to him there at West Coast, but you ought to be ashamed. So don't ring here again!'"

Hardly subtle, but it had to be said. Next time Clive or anyone else from the Company wished to speak to me, they would have to do it during office hours – that's if there *was* a next time.

Although I tried to shrug it off, I couldn't help but find Clive's early-morning call decidedly creepy, especially coming so soon after my troubled dream. In fact, I felt so agitated that I couldn't resist sharing my concern with Mum. As always, she did her level best to put my mind at ease, assuring me that any apparent link between my dream and Clive's telephone call was purely coincidental.

However, I wasn't convinced. I felt certain there was something more … something intangible … a powerful force summoning my psyche back to the pool.

I had shared a unique bond with my Atlanteans – a special *connection* that couldn't be terminated simply by the closing of a door. This particularly held true when it came to Duchess.

In my despair, I had fled without so much as a goodbye, leaving her at the mercy of people who neither cared nor understood, which meant she'd be increasingly anxious for my return – a return that now looked to be impossible. Yet, despite this, there could be no peace for either of us until we'd found each other again.

To make matters worse, I was still smarting about her behaviour towards Herb'e, choosing to view events through human instead of Atlantean eyes – a convenience my jumbled mind had all too readily embraced.

I'd become angry, frustrated and desperate to find a scapegoat for my failings – and, with typical human logic, I'd chosen the one I cherished above all others … my greatest love … my poor, abandoned Duchess.

❧ 148 ❧

Thank God it's night-time – it's been another horrible, draining day, not made any pleasanter by the mystery of Clive's telephone call. I mean, if Clive so desperately wanted to talk to me, then why didn't he 'phone again today? It just doesn't make sense.

Then there's that dream – uncannily real.

God, what's wrong with me? Why can't I let it go? I'm supposed to be trying to put the horrors of West Coast behind me, get back to some semblance of normality. I need to forget about the lousy Company, because the dolphin project is no longer any of my business – I'm out of it! What I need now is to rest my tortured mind … shut out the world. Sleep.

…

My eyes have barely closed, yet I'm aware of my arms flailing – I'm falling headlong through murky shadows … down, down, down into black waters.

Within the liquid chromite, I see faces – a montage of grotesque, twisted faces. Drowned souls from the Id – some laughing, some leering, all pointing … aiming the finger of accusation. Their hideous cackle is tearing through the void.

"Backhouse! Backhouse! Give it a rest, Capello – you're always whining about Backhouse. Course he was a schemer … Course he was ambitious … So what's new?"

"Yeah, Backhouse wasn't the only one. What about your precious Gerry? He was just as bad! That's why he hated Backhouse so much – he viewed him as a rival … a threat."

"But do you know what really takes the biscuit, Capello? They both saw *you* as the biggest threat of all! You were just too blind to see it."

His face ... I see Herb'e's grinning face. His death mask.

Drowning ... drowning ... being sucked down a vortex and desperately need someone to get me out. But nobody's helping ... They're just standing and staring ... What's wrong with them? Why won't they help? Why won't ...

...

Am I swimming, or am I floating? I'm not sure, because I can't feel anything. All I know is that I'm looking down – down from high above the West Coast arena.

I'm aware of dolphin snorts echoing through the silence, yet no sound reaches my ears. From this elevated perch, I can clearly see Duchess schooling alongside Scouse, their sleek bodies trailing soft patterns across the water ... But there's no trace of ...

A scream rips through my head ...

... I'm in a new location, a familiar location – the stage.

She's awake ... and she's been waiting for me.

"I can't believe what you did, Duchess. How you treated him. Herb'e would have followed you to the ends of the earth. He sacrificed everything for you – even his freedom. So why did you desert him?"

That deafening thunder – the same drumroll I experienced during my last visit – totally obliterating her reply.

Still, what do I care? I'm not here for *her*; I'm here to give the Company hell ...

The stage netting – some poor fool must have taken a long time to rehang it ... Well, it's coming down – all of it! – along with everything else that belongs to me!

"Stop it, David, stop it now! You can't do this!"

Wha ...? Where did *they* come from? Two presenters, calling me by name ...

Got to get out of here ... escape while the going's good ...

...

Whoa! It was virtually the same dream – *me* wrecking the West Coast stage. So real that I can actually feel where the netting has cut into my fingers ... What the hell's going on?

A ringing ... a telephone ringing ...

Oh, no, it's happening again.

Mum's just gone tearing past my room …

She's speaking – not whispering like she did before, but talking so loudly that I can hear every word.

"*No, no*, Mr Rothwell, I told you yesterday, you *can't* speak to David – it's five in the morning and he's in bed! Have you any idea how ill he is? You and your rotten dolphinarium have nearly killed my son … and, I'm warning you, if you call here again, I *will* take steps."

It's suddenly gone very quiet, which means Mum must have hung up on him.

Either way, this is the second time Clive's telephoned me directly after my dream. It's uncanny … It can't be just a coincidence – something else has to be going on …

Perhaps my dream isn't just a dream after all.

⟨ 149 ⟩

I'd only been on home soil for two nights, yet my shattered mind had found it impossible to escape the draw of the West Coast dolphinarium.

It was as if I'd become a split personality: two tortured psyches, each with a different agenda – the first craving freedom from its self-imposed incarceration; the other, a fury fixed solely on revenge.

A restless anger dwelt within me – a gnawing heartache that was using the twilight hours to revisit the scene of my greatest failure.

All the evidence in the West Coast haunting now pointed firmly towards me, which raised an interesting question: would I allow my inner-fury the luxury of a third assault on the stricken pool, knowing that Clive and his people would be waiting to expose me?

You're damn right I would!

⟨ 150 ⟩

What a weird feeling! I've been like a cat on hot bricks waiting for nightfall – excited even. If I *am* astral projecting (which I'm pretty sure I am), there will be those at West Coast eagerly awaiting my reappearance – sceptics who believe that there's a perfectly logical explanation for what they've witnessed over the past two nights. "After all," they'll ask themselves, "how can anyone be in two places at the same time?" The very reason for those early-morning telephone calls from Clive – he was checking my whereabouts.

Clive knows that my house is a good two hours' drive from West Coast, which means he didn't believe Mum when she told him that I was home in bed. Obviously, he suspected I was hiding out somewhere in the West Coast area.

What a shock he's gonna get when he discovers otherwise!

It's exhilarating – for the first time in three days, I actually feel alive. Nevertheless, I need to prepare myself ... rest my tortured mind ... shut out the world. Sleep.

...

My eyes have barely closed, yet I'm aware of my arms flailing – I'm falling headlong through murky shadows ... down, down, down into black waters.

Within the liquid chromite, I see faces – a montage of grotesque, twisted faces. Drowned souls from the Id – some laughing, some leering, all pointing ... aiming the finger of accusation. Their hideous cackle is tearing through the void.

"Well, would you believe it? Mr Capello come back to visit ... back to right all his wrongs."

"Why did you even bother, Capello? Don't you think you've done enough damage? After all, you're one of the main reasons that the dolphin circus is so popular."

"Yeah, if it hadn't been for your obsession with the shadow ballet, the public would never have flocked to your shows in such numbers."

"Face it, Capello, the plight of the captive dolphin is down to people like you — idealists who choose to view the world through rose-tinted glasses."

"Hah! The men in suits certainly hit the jackpot when they got their hands on a fool like you."

His face ... I see Herb'e's grinning face. His death mask.

Drowning ... drowning ... being sucked down a vortex and desperately need someone to get me out. But nobody's helping ... They're just standing and staring ... What's wrong with them? Why won't they help? Why won't ...

...

Am I swimming, or am I floating? I'm not sure, because I can't feel anything. All I know is that I'm looking down — down from high above the West Coast arena.

I'm aware of dolphin snorts echoing through the silence, yet no sound reaches my ears. From this elevated perch, I can clearly see Duchess schooling alongside Scouse, their sleek bodies trailing soft patterns across the water ... But there's no trace of ...

A scream rips through my head ...

... I'm in a new location — the stage.

She's distressed, clearly distressed.

"Please, David, don't be angry with me. There's no reason for you to be angry. You know that I would never do anything to hurt you."

That clap of thunder again swamps her words, but I have to give Duchess a chance to explain — push the demon noise from my head — because *she* isn't the one I'm angry with ... it's *me* I'm angry with — I just never wanted to admit it.

It wasn't Duchess who let Herb'e down on that transport — it was me. I went missing when he needed me most, left him vulnerable and unprotected ... abandoned him to the spite of Backhouse.

I should have put my foot down with Philip Haynes, refused point-blank to go to hospital. But I didn't. Instead, I placated him.

How can I ever forgive myself?

"David, you can't keep shouldering the blame. Herb'e chose to move on. What's done is done. You have to let it go."

She's right ... Duchess is right – I have to let it go. Yet how can I when her *connection* keeps drawing me back?

"Duchess, my mind just can't take it anymore – it's closing up. You have to release me or I'll go insane ... Please, Duchess, only you can help me ... Please!"

"David, you've got to stop this madness – stop it now!"

People ... people jumping out of the shadows ... Got to get out ... make for the auditorium!

"David, please, please ... We need to talk ..."

That voice ... I recognise that voice – it's Clive, my ex-manager, my friend.

Can't seem to move my legs ... it's as if my feet are welded to the ground. God, I'm looking straight at him ... straight into his eyes. What am I gonna do? *What* am I gonna do?

Tell him, that's what ... tell him of the torture I'm going through ... But there's no sound, no words coming out of my mouth. What's wrong with me? Why can't I speak?

So confused ... just need to escape this horrible, horrible place ... get away as fast as I can ...

...

My aching head – it feels like it's about to explode ... but I'm back in bed and the dream is over. Now, let's see ... see if that telephone rings ... see if Clive confirms what I already know to be true.

There! And right on cue – five o'clock in the morning! The ringing of the telephone.

God, if a sound could paint a picture!

There she goes – Mum scurrying past my door ...

Any minute now ...

"He's done *what*? That's impossible ... he's never stepped outside this house for the past three days."

Mum's shouting – what the heck has Clive just said?

"David, sorry to wake you – it's Clive Rothwell again ... but this time, I think you're going to have to speak to him ...

... he's just accused you of trashing the West Coast pool."

ᚹ 151 ᚹ

Forcing a reassuring smile, I tentatively took the telephone receiver from Mum's hand.

"Hello, Clive. Judging by the time, I can only gather that this isn't a social call. So what's the problem?"

I heard the gasp – his sudden loss of breath at the shock of hearing my voice.

"David? *David?* I … I don't understand … How can you be there? I've just seen you not ten minutes ago here in the dolphinarium."

"You've seen *me* at West Coast? I'm sorry, Clive, but that's impossible. I've never left this house for three days, let alone made it to West Coast."

"But I did, David … and I'm not the only one – others have seen you too. You've been here for the last three nights smashing up the stage – that's why I'm calling you so early in the morning, to verify your whereabouts."

I could faintly hear the confused whispers echoing down the telephone line, meaning that my ex-manager wasn't alone.

"Clive, before you and your entourage make any more accusations, just ask yourselves: if I'm talking to you from City, how the heck can I possibly be at West Coast? I mean, it's over two hours away, for God's sake. What you're saying is ludicrous. How can anyone be in two places at the same time?"

Clive didn't answer, but I could plainly hear the heightened kerfuffle of background voices feeding down the line.

"Clive, I've been so wrecked since I got home that I've barely set foot outside my bedroom, so, whoever you think you saw at the dolphinarium, it most definitely couldn't be me."

"But it was … it was *you* … I swear it! I spoke to you myself as you were running towards the auditorium. *And* I've seen you on at least one other occasion trashing this dolphinarium."

I didn't reply, but let him stew in his confusion.

"I just don't understand … don't understand any of this. I *saw* you … large as life."

Poor, bewildered Clive – he must have thought he was losing his mind.

"Clive, this has been a nightmare for us all, so why don't you and your friends stop hiding in corners and go home to bed. Whoever you thought you saw is long gone by now and won't risk coming back."

A bold prediction to make – especially in light of my unstable psyche – yet I'd never been more sure of anything in my life. The frustrated soul that had taken to venting its wrath upon the West Coast stage had at last been sated, which meant I'd never again have to inflict myself on that wretched dolphinarium …

… a welcome blessing, I would imagine, for a much-beleaguered West Coast Management.

❦ 152 ❧

It would have been pointless trying to explain to Clive just what had really happened, because I didn't fully understand it myself. However, as incredible as it might seem, I had indeed been responsible for trashing the West Coast pool – a fact unwittingly confirmed by my ex-manager.

He, along with others, had witnessed exactly what I'd experienced during my dreams – the traumatised apparition of my broken self. They had lain in wait to catch a poltergeist … and had instead found *me* – a fact that made my mother's role in this drama all the more vital.

Mum had now become the number one witness for my defence. She was the only one who knew the true significance of my "dream"; plus she had actually spoken to Clive Rothwell on all three relevant occasions, therefore assuring me of a cast-iron alibi.

She knew that I could *not* have physically committed the wanton destruction of which I was accused … She knew that I was innocent …

Or did she?

I was under no illusions that her "not guilty" verdict might well be overturned by the removal of just one word – "physically".

Clive was no liar. When he swore that he'd challenged me on that final night, he was telling the truth.

I *had been* at West Coast.

I vividly remembered the stricken expression on his face as I'd fled towards that darkened auditorium. Yes, there was no doubt in my mind that I'd been there and hell-bent on revenge.

So, when seemingly holding the upper hand, why had I suddenly abandoned my task of retribution? Why had I banished my astral avenger back to the locker?

I thought I knew the answer.

Although fuelled by heartbreak, the destructive fury that had so possessed me had originally been seeded by love – a profound and spiritual love that had always bound my Atlanteans and me together.

But, alas, as so often with stories of the heart, there was to be no happy ending – our precious union had been tainted by greed and ambition, and somewhere in the mêlée, I had lost my way.

Despite this, I liked to think that it was Duchess' love that had spirited my soul through that astral wormhole; that it was she who had braved the perils of time and space to draw me back to her side. Feeling my pain, she had summoned my psyche to grant it the peace it so craved by revoking what had once been my most cherished possession – the gift of her *connection*.

It seemed that my princess had heard my plea after all.

From her concrete cell, my greatest love had made the ultimate sacrifice, forever closing the doors to my mind and releasing me from her gentle embrace.

My beautiful, beautiful, abandoned Duchess … I would never hear her song again.

❦ 153 ❧

Torment now usurped by guilt, I tried my hand at re-joining the hurly-burly of the human race, signing on at my local dole office as an unemployed dolphin trainer and feverishly praying that a vacancy wouldn't appear. (Although I needn't have prayed too hard as there was little call for dolphin trainers in my suburban town.)

Nevertheless, my already dire finances had now hit a new low – a situation exacerbated by Backhouse's enthusiastic gallop to clarify that the Company had *not* sacked me, but that I'd walked of my own accord, thus rendering me ineligible for unemployment benefit. So, practically broke, I begrudgingly cut short my three-week sabbatical to re-start work as a signwriter and illustrator with Dad.

It struck me as incredible that, despite having trained one of Europe's greatest dolphin shows, I'd ended up both skint and unrecognised. Even so, this was a small price to pay if it meant having escaped the Company's clutches.

Escaped? How wrong could I have been? After all, Head Office was only ever a 'phone call away.

"Hello, am I speaking to Mr David Capello?"

Yet another unfamiliar voice representing a Company I loathed.

"I've been instructed to inform you that you are now barred from all Company dolphinariums."

Barred? *Barred?* This smacked of Backhouse – even with me gone, he was still pursuing his pound of flesh.

"That seems a bit extreme. Can I ask why?"

"It's quite simple – the wanton vandalism of the West Coast pool, along with the theft of the Flippa logbooks, for which we believe *you* to be responsible."

300

So it seemed that the charge of vandalism had stuck, which meant that even Clive had turned against me, choosing to believe his eyes rather than his ears. And now, to boot, I was being blamed for the disappearance of Herb'e's chronicles.

"Mr Capello, if you do indeed have these logbooks in your possession, I would strongly advise that you return them immediately, otherwise the Company will be forced to take the matter further. Do I make myself clear?"

Head Office was clearly rattled – terrified that Herb'e's diaries would one day be used against them. Little wonder, as they revealed every grubby detail of the Company's exploitive push to make money.

I made no comment, but instead slammed down the receiver with a theatrical panache. I couldn't help but smirk as I contemplated just what might happen should those logbooks indeed ever fall into the "wrong" hands.

But, as the words of that faceless executive struck home, my smug satisfaction evaporated all too quickly. This official barring meant that, no matter what the circumstances, the Company would never allow me to see Duchess, Baby or Scouse again – a truly tragic situation for us all.

Still reeling from Head Office's threats, I slowly made my way upstairs to seek the sanctuary of my bedroom. Once inside, I hesitantly opened the doors of my wardrobe to reveal the battered holdall that I'd so hurriedly packed on that fateful morning of Herb'e's death. Carefully and reverently, I placed it on my bed, before slowly unzipping it to gaze down on its contents …

There they were: the guardians of the Company's conscience – the seven missing chronicles cataloguing Herb'e's entire life in captivity.

It seemed that my time spent dealing with men like Backhouse had prepared me well. Even in the throes of my torment, I'd instinctively snatched what I believed to be mine.

Deep down, I had never had the slightest intention of allowing the Corporate Beast to destroy Herb'e's memory, to erase the life of this extraordinary Atlantean. For within these priceless books lay the documented evidence of Britain's greatest show dolphin, and commandeering them would one day allow me to write – not just Herb'e's story – but *their* story … the story of Duchess and Herb'e, Europe's greatest dolphin team …

… a magical story entitled *The Perfect Pair*.

❧ 154 ❧

Strange how seven dog-eared diaries could invoke the smell of salt air and visions of Atlanteans now lost or left behind: Herb'e, Baby, Scouse and, of course, Duchess.

Duchess … No matter how hard I tried to push her from my mind, I couldn't help but wonder how she was coping without me. I'd promised never to leave her, yet here I was … gone – banished forever by a vindictive Head Office.

My poor princess! It seemed that her expectations of me were far greater than I was ever able to deliver.

But, banished or not, I knew that there was no way I could ever again walk back onto a dolphinarium stage, as to do so would not only condone an industry I had come to hate, but also betray the Atlanteans I'd been forced to abandon. No, I was determined that – no matter what the temptation – there would be no more dolphinarium exploits for me.

Yet the fates had other ideas.

"David, come to the front door quick! You've got a telegram!"

Mum was over the moon. But she wasn't the only one – a telegram, for goodness' sake! I'd never even *seen* a telegram, let alone received one.

The excitement was palpable as my whole family crowded behind me to peer over my shoulders.

"Well, come on, open it!" Mum urged. "We haven't got all day, and we want to know what it says …"

So much for my privacy – no one was budging until I'd revealed the missive's hidden secret.

Certificate of Authenticity

Presented to

David Mather

This certificate has been issued to authenticate that this book

is one of a specially limited series of two hundred Matador hardback copies
by authors,
David C Holroyd and Tracy J Holroyd

Authorised signatures

Tracy J. Holroyd

"Right, folks, are you ready?" I put on my best presenter voice. "The post office stamp is dated 1st October 1974, and the telegram reads as follows:

POSITION OF HEAD DOLPHIN AND KILLER WHALE TRAINER NOW VACANT STOP GOOD SALARY AND ACCOMMODATION STOP IF INTERESTED PLEASE PHONE ME *GAVIN STARK WINSTON SAFARI PARK WINSTON* ★★★★★

I held my breath – a killer whale … an actual killer whale! As far as I was aware, Europe currently had only one captive orca, and, incredibly, I was being asked to train it. Still in a state of shock, I rechecked the telegram's contents. I still couldn't believe it: a killer whale – a genuine killer whale – the most striking cetacean of them all.

Gavin Stark bore the name of the most famous circus family in Europe and would have had the pick of the world's top trainers, yet he had chosen to seek *me* out. What an opportunity! I had at last been recognised by those who mattered …

… judged by my peers to be the best of the best.

For me, this was a dream come true. Now, all I had to do was claim my prize and bask in the distinction of having landed the greatest training job in Europe … possibly even the world.

However, the big question now was … did I actually want it?

❧ 155 ❧

Although I'd sworn never again to visit a dolphinarium, I couldn't pass up this unique opportunity to view such a magnificent Atlantean. So, with the Stark family footing the bill, I eagerly boarded the train to embark on my last venture into the world of the aqua-circus – a calling I'd originally answered over three and a half years ago from those self-same grime-trodden platforms of City Railway Station.

It was like rolling back the years: I could clearly see him – that starry-eyed kid, excitedly stepping into his chariot in pursuit of fame and fortune. Who would have believed that in such a short space of time he would have achieved his ultimate goal – to be hailed as one of Europe's finest trainers? It beggared belief … Was that really *me*? I was still having trouble taking it all in.

My life was about to change big-style. I would soon be plunged into a completely different world, as graphically illustrated by the changing scenery now flashing past the carriage windows. That dingy picture of a depressed northern town was gradually blossoming into a cleaner, brighter landscape – a lush southern vista that oozed wealth.

Yes, being summoned to this Royal Borough by this celebrated circus family was unmistakeably the pinnacle of my career – a fantasy realised … So why did I still harbour doubts?

Having arrived at Winston station, I was greeted by a park representative, who then chauffeured me to the biggest purpose-built arena in the country – a hugely impressive structure that housed one of the world's most majestic creatures: Ramu III – Europe's only killer whale.

Except for an unnaturally collapsed dorsal fin, Ramu's sheer presence was little short of breathtaking.

"He's magnificent, absolutely magnificent!" I enthused.

The young presenter who was acting as my guide hesitantly ushered me forward for a closer look.

"Now, be careful," he warned. "This whale's dangerous ... You can't trust him."

The lad's dread was tangible, as well as disappointing. Fear was a mind-killer that had to be avoided at all costs. So, leaving him firmly rooted to the rear of the stage, I excitedly took three steps into the unknown.

"Hello, my son ... Well, aren't you beautiful?"

Bang! The huge Atlantean's bulk abruptly shuddered to a halt, generating a mini-tsunami that smashed over the tank walls. Amazing ... I was *in* − a super speed *connection,* as if my radio had never been offline.

The alien mirror exploded skywards as the black and white powerhouse swung violently around to bullet towards me.

"Whoa! Slow down, sunshine ... let's not get too excited!"

It was incredible − my brief time away from my charges had in no way compromised my ability to link with the Atlantean mind. In fact, if anything, it had been strengthened − my *connection* seemed sharper than ever, meaning that my enforced rest had indeed worked the oracle.

Behind me, the young presenter emitted a panicky howl.

"Look out ... he's coming! Don't get too close, or he'll 'ave you!"

This kid was seriously unnerving: he wasn't just frightened; he was petrified. And, what's more, the orca knew it, sliding his massive head onto the stage in a gleeful effort to intimidate.

As I experienced the electricity of Ramu's wild *connection,* I couldn't help but flash him a wicked smile.

"I know your game, big fella ... Go ahead − have some fun!"

The orca's response was again immediate: brazenly opening his mouth, he flashed a set of razor-sharp teeth, before giving the terrified presenter a long, hard tongue pull.

Not only did this whale have fire in his belly, but he was extremely intelligent as well. Ramu and I had only just met, yet he'd already recognised that I was somehow different from those he'd known before − an insight that had him nodding his head feverishly in anticipation of forthcoming exploits.

This colossus was certainly a prize …

… but was he a *gentle* giant?

I wasn't so sure, because, even at this early stage, my inbuilt defences were yelling "complications" – my senses were literally being bombarded by a mishmash of chaotic emotion.

Was this down to Ramu's sheer exuberance … or was it something else?

This killer whale had not seen his own kind for an age, which meant that his mental state would be extremely fragile – a condition not aided by his achingly cramped surroundings …

He screamed of psychosis.

Ramu's inner turmoil meant that I would have to tread carefully. Maybe the young presenter was right after all …

… maybe this whale *was* dangerous.

❧ 156 ❧

"I see you made it, then."

There was no mistaking those dulcet tones, or his inherent ability to light up a room: Will Chadderton – it certainly lifted the heart to see him.

"Hello, Will, what the heck are *you* doing here? Last time I saw you, you were acting referee in a Hendle free-for-all."

Those trademark orbs beamed with mischievous delight. "Oh, David, don't even go there! What a nightmare! I honestly thought you were gonna do Backhouse in."

My ex-Hendle-manager was certainly bang-on there, 'cause after what Backhouse had put me through, my *not* pushing him into that empty pool had been nothing short of a miracle.

Amazingly, this was the first time I'd actually seen Will since that traumatic night, so I felt I had a lot of apologising to do – but, as usual, he was way ahead of me.

"Well, it's good to see you, David – and, before you say another word, just you forget about what happened with Backhouse, because it's all water under the bridge now. The only thing that matters is that *you're* here at Winston."

Furtively checking for the whereabouts of my terrified chaperone, Will leaned forward to whisper in my ear.

"Now, keep this to yourself … The reason I got here so early was to tip you off about the kind of salary you should expect."

I gave him a puzzled look.

"Salary? Good grief, hold your horses – I haven't been offered the job yet, and the Starks must have a whole host of big-name trainers waiting in the wings."

Roughing me exuberantly by the shoulders, Will grinned.

"No, they haven't – there's only one person in the frame for this orca job, and that's *you*. The Starks have *already* made their decision. They've been monitoring your work for some time, and are prepared to pay you big bucks – so don't sell yourself short."

Will was obviously party to some serious insider dealing, because he seemed ultra-sure of his facts.

"Are you certain? Because last I heard, you'd left the Company, and – I assumed – the business."

"Yes, I *am* certain!" Will indulged me with yet another shifty glance. "I might have left the Company, but I certainly *didn't* leave the business. I reinvented myself as a freelance filtration advisor, which means I now get to work for *all* the commercial dolphinariums – not just those belonging to the Company. And, as an added bonus, I get to hear *all* the juicy gossip."

"What about the Starks? Do they know what happened with Backhouse … what I did to him?"

My ex-manager rolled his eyes skywards. "Of course they know what happened with Backhouse. For goodness' sake, David, *everyone* knows – it's the worst-kept secret in the business … so quit worrying! The only thing the Starks are interested in is what you can do for their whale. Believe me, an awful lot of people have put their reputations on the line to get you this job – *me* included. As you can imagine, your being invited here has caused ructions at City Head Office. Word has it that the Board is now demanding to know how the Company managed to lose Europe's top-rated trainer to a major competitor. Backhouse, in particular, is livid – he's been calling just about everyone to try to get you shut out of the business."

I couldn't help but smirk – the thought of Backhouse and Rogers up to their necks in hot water certainly warmed the cockles of my heart. I just hoped that they'd finally get their comeuppance – but knowing how plausible and slippery Backhouse could be, I wouldn't be holding my breath.

"Good morning, David, glad to see you down here so bright and early."

This couldn't be happening! Yet another friendly voice: Philip Haynes, large as life and standing on the Winston stage.

"Sorry I haven't been in contact for some time, but I've been working in the Middle East. The Sultan of Brunei is having problems with his prize llamas and racing camels, but I flew back because I wanted to be here when you met the Starks. I've spoken to them about you on numerous occasions, and wanted to introduce you personally."

The Sultan of Brunei – that sounded *very* lucrative. Yet, here he was – the ever-popular playboy vet – braving the rainy UK just to give me a reference.

It was uplifting: here were two men – both experts in their own fields – who truly believed in me, so the last thing I wanted to do was let them down.

Let them down ... let them down ...

I now had an incredibly difficult decision to make – one that would shape my life forever.

clyde rules

❧ 157 ❧

"David, I've got to be honest, there's a special reason why you were chosen for this job. As you've no doubt gathered, this killer whale is used to ruling the roost, so the Starks are desperate to find a trainer that he can't intimidate. That's why they want *you* – not just because of what you achieved with Duchess and Herb'e, but because *you* were the only trainer ever to keep Clyde in check."

Keep Clyde in check? I wasn't too sure I could take all the credit for that – my six months or so working with Clyde nearly finished me, and if it hadn't been for Bonnie, I would never have gotten through.

"You're a gifted trainer, David, and most probably the only one out there capable of sorting this orca out."

Just as Will had done only minutes earlier, Philip flung a reassuring arm around my shoulder.

"Ramu needs someone with the ability to climb inside his head … feel what he's feeling. Believe me, David, this whale is made for you."

Sandwiched between my two sponsors, I felt like the proverbial lamb to the slaughter. Despite their efforts to play it cool, it was becoming ever more obvious that my two amigos were now subjecting me to a two-pronged charm offensive.

Nevertheless, I had to admit that Philip's assertion rang true: this whale was indeed made for me. Training him would be my ultimate challenge – should I choose to accept it. Yet I seriously had to ask myself: would my psyche be able to withstand another barrage of mental punishment? After all, Herb'e's death was still an open wound, not to mention the racking guilt I was suffering about deserting Duchess … I mean, how could I ever look into another Atlantean's eyes and *not* see her face reflecting back?

I wrestled with my conscience. What should I do? Because, amazingly, even after all I'd been through, I was still finding it near impossible to resist the thrill of this whale's Atlantean song.

Financially, taking on Ramu would be my biggest-ever payday. Will had already assured me that Gavin Stark was prepared to pay me more than triple my earnings at West Coast … not counting the complimentary luxury trailer home based in the park grounds. Yet this wasn't about money – it had *never* been about money … So what should I do?

Will and Philip were now uncomfortably aware that I was struggling to make a decision, so the vet launched himself into one final appeal.

"David, please, *please* think carefully before you give your answer. It just doesn't come any bigger than this. If you accept this position, you'll have it all – fame, money, girls … and recognition as Europe's finest."

The vet was right – but neither was I under any illusion as to what would happen should I refuse it: I would effectively be ending my career.

"David, David …" he persisted, "there are trainers out there who would kill to get their hands on this whale. Think … just think about everything you'll be throwing away if you turn it down. You'll be proclaiming to the world that you're finished with the dolphinarium industry."

I couldn't speak, but answered my two friends with a "thanks, but no thanks" smile.

I'd made my choice.

How could I trade-in the beloved Atlanteans I'd left behind for another – no matter what his size and prestige?

No, I couldn't.

Subconsciously, I'd already made my decision on the night of Herb'e's death.

So it was now official – my journey with the citizens of Atlantis was over. For me, it was back to that dirty old town and home sweet home … not to mention, at long last, peace of mind.

❧ 158 ❧

It had been a full six weeks since I'd walked out of West Coast and, despite the Company's threat to the contrary, I'd heard nothing more about Herb'e's missing logbooks – no doubt thanks to my having rejected the Starks' lucrative orca contract. I was well aware that my old employers had benefited greatly from this decision, because my continued presence in the ranks of trainers would have proved to be a constant embarrassment to them.

Even so, I had no regrets, as it meant that I'd finally escaped this exploitive industry *and* the manipulative individuals who controlled it. My torment was over – unlike that of my poor Atlanteans.

"David, it's for you ... telephone!"

Even from under my headphones, it was impossible not to hear Mum's call to arms, meaning that my imaginary gig with Keith Emerson on keyboard would have to be cut short.

"Coming, Mum ... Who is it?"

No answer, my words ravenously gobbled up by the repetitive thumping of Mum's beleaguered washing machine.

"Hello, David Capello here. Can I help you?"

"Hello, buggerlugs! I bet you can't guess who this is?"

Surely not ... It couldn't be ... could it?

"Come on, Capello, don't tell me you've forgotten your old mucker already? Blimey, you don't get off the hook that easily."

"Vance! Vance! I can't tell you how good it is to hear from you." The sound of his voice gave me a buzz I found impossible to disguise. "What are you up to these days?"

Vance's reply was literally the last thing I expected.

"Well, Dave, you won't believe it, but I'm working at West Coast. I've been here for the last three weeks trying to bring the shows back online – something I'm not having much success with, which is the reason, my old cocker, why I'm calling *you*."

Unreal! Vance Martin working at my old pool – it beggared belief.

"How on earth did you end up at West Coast? I mean, how did you manage to get past Backhouse?"

Vance's tone changed markedly at the mention of our former general manager.

"*Him*! I don't think old *Shithouse* even knows that I'm here. Clive Rothwell brought me in – probably because I'm the only one who understands your training methods. I'm telling you, Dave, after you walked, the pool fell into absolute chaos. Duchess and Scouse wouldn't work without you, and the dolphinarium was losing a fortune. Management went ballistic."

Chaos! Exactly what I'd warned Clive would happen if he allowed Rogers and Backhouse to force me out. Nevertheless, the men in suits wouldn't want to blame this disaster on the shenanigans of their two fellow executives. As usual, they'd be searching for a scapegoat, and I could hear the whole, rotten, sorry bunch whining even now: "This is all Capello's fault … He let us down big-style … How could he have left us in such a mess?" Yes, it wasn't hard to imagine the flames of blame now wafting around the hallowed halls of Head Office.

"Dave, I'm sorry to put this on you, but I've no one else to turn to. Things here are awful, and I don't know how much more I can take. The atmosphere's horrible, and I'm desperate to talk to somebody I can trust."

Vance's distress was all too familiar – his three-week stint at West Coast was obviously taking its toll. My old colleague needed support – but before I gave it, *I* needed answers … starting with Duchess.

"Vance, before we go any further, I need to know how Duchess is coping without me? Is she eating?"

Vance's next words chilled me to my core.

"Dave … Duchess *isn't* here."

159

Duchess isn't here ... Duchess isn't here ...

Vance's revelation was a hammer-blow, pulverizing any chance of a quick-fire response.

Duchess isn't here ... Duchess isn't here ...

Yet how could that be? I'd only been gone from West Coast for six weeks, leaving three weeks at most before Vance had started working there.

Acutely aware of the hit he'd just delivered, my ex-partner jumped in to try to reassure me.

"Dave, there's nothing to worry about. Like I said, Duchess and Scouse wouldn't work without you, so Management sent them back to Hendle."

Thank goodness! My two former charges returned to their old stomping-ground, well away from that cursed pool.

"Believe me, it's pandemonium here," Vance complained. "There's been a complete change of staff – and most of them don't know one end of a dolphin from the other. Plus I *never* see Clive Rothwell anymore, because he's delegated the running of the dolphinarium to a new under-manager – a fairground wallah and a total waste of space if ever there was one. What's more, he doesn't like me – not one bit – and, I've got to say, the feeling's mutual."

Much as I sympathised with my ex-partner's predicament, my two lost Atlanteans still had to be my Number One priority.

"Look, Vance, I'm sorry to hear that – I really am – but I *have* to know how Duchess and Scouse are getting on without me. I need you to put my mind at rest. Do you know if they're eating normally? Surely you can help me out – all you have to do is pick up the 'phone and ask whoever's in charge of the dolphins at Hendle."

"It's not that easy, Dave. For one thing, I might end up talking to Backhouse, and you *know* how that's gonna finish. As for the bloke who's handling the dolphins, well, he's new and not known for being helpful. The grapevine has it that he's a mouthy sod, and, from what they say, he won't have anything to do with West Coast – probably because there's still bad blood bubbling over the way Backhouse and Rogers treated you. Sorry, Dave, telephoning Hendle is a definite no-no."

I was amazed to hear that the fallout from my clash with Backhouse was continuing unabated. However, the mention of Hendle's new handler immediately sparked my curiosity.

"This new bloke – what's his name? Is he a trainer, or just one of Backhouse's puppet-presenters?"

"I'm told he's called Tom Darley. As for being a trainer, I haven't got a clue – but knowing what a phobia Backhouse has of trainers, I very much doubt it."

Tom Darley – I'd never heard that name before, but he was undoubtedly the individual chosen by the Company to oversee its hideous wintering policy, a madness that would see all the West Coast dolphins incarcerated with the Hendle dolphins during the closed season. Still, nothing I could do about that now... Nothing I could do about anything, for that matter.

"Vance, try to look on the bright side. At least things have turned out right for old Scouse – him getting back with Baby is a real bonus, no matter how you look at it. About time the little mite had a bit of luck."

I sensed an uncomfortable pause; but my ex-partner chose not to elaborate, so I moved the conversation on.

"Anyway, Vance, who became lead team at West Coast, because, last I heard, Hendle was struggling to put a show together?"

He gave a cynical laugh.

"Hah! Hendle is *still* struggling to put a show together. Let's face it, they never recovered from the loss of Duchess and Herb'e. But, to answer your question, the new West Coast team was *supposed* to be Eccles and Blodwyn – or Big Mamma, as we once knew her."

Big Mamma – I recalled Gerry Mansell calling me in once to make a catch on her because she had a reputation for being aggressive. As for Eccles, he was the dolphin that Gerry had so enthused about in those early days, and one of the Atlanteans I'd shamefully neglected after losing my coveted Baby and Scouse team.

"Anyway, Dave, the Blodwyn and Eccles team didn't last, because Blodwyn turned out to be a vicious bully. Every time Eccles attempted his highball, she tried to ram him in mid-air. In fact, she became so psychotic that the vets actually started dosing her with Librium. Only problem was, the Librium didn't work, which meant that poor Eccles spent most of his time either fleeing around the pool or hiding in corners. Finally, in fear for his life, the vets recommended his immediate return to Hendle ... But you're never gonna believe who Management sent to replace him?"

"Who? 'Cause, as far as I can see, there's only ..." My heart plummeted. "Oh, Vance, please, *please*, don't tell me that they sent Baby ..."

❦ 160 ❧

"Got it in one, Dave!"

I felt a rush of air sieve through my teeth.

"Hold on, Vance … hold on …You're *telling* me that they actually banged an infant dolphin with a full-grown adult so off its head that it has to be pumped full of drugs? Are they all insane or what? I mean whose bright idea was that?"

An unbelievably silly question – there was only *one* person who could have authorised such a crazy pairing … Backhouse!

"Dave, I told them a million times that putting Baby with Blodwyn was sheer madness, but they refused to listen. All they kept saying was that there were no other dolphins trained to show standard and that the authorisation had come direct from Head Office. I'm telling you, Dave, you can't imagine what it's been like in this bloody place … I don't know whether I'm coming or going."

I couldn't agree with him there – I *knew* all too well what it was like in "that bloody place"! However, that aside, for a conversation that had started out so jovially, we were now racing headlong into the pits – and I had a feeling that it was gonna get worse before it got better.

"Vance, a decision as crass as this could have only come from Backhouse, which means you're gonna have to bypass this new manager and go straight to the top. You have to talk to Clive Rothwell – and pronto! Believe me, if you don't get Baby away from that psycho dolphin, there'll be murder."

"It's too late for that, Dave … the shit's already hit the fan."

Finally, we were getting there – the *real* reason for Vance's call.

"During one of the late shows, Baby was making his highball jump when Blodwyn rammed him in mid-air, knocking him clean out of the pool. It was horrific – I honestly thought she'd killed him. Baby hit the stage like a sack of potatoes and there was blood everywhere. The audience started screaming and I just didn't know what to do."

Poor Vance! Poor *Baby*! It sounded like something out of a horror movie.

"All I could do was shove Baby back into the water and get the public out as fast as I could. Believe me, it was a nightmare. The vet said Baby had been lucky – as far as he could tell, his injuries were only superficial."

Lucky? He'd been lucky all right – lucky to be alive. The potential consequences of a mid-air ramming coupled with a crunching fall onto a rock-hard stage didn't bear thinking about. At the very least, Baby would have suffered from serious cuts and bruising, to say nothing of possible broken bones and other internal injuries.

"God, Vance, what an ordeal! So what happened? Did they send Baby back to Hendle?"

Vance sounded choked.

"No, they didn't send him back to Hendle – they just stuck to the excuse that they didn't have any other dolphins that were show worthy."

I sighed. "Vance, you *have* to talk to Clive. You must try to get Baby away from Blodwyn, or she *will* do it again."

"Don't you think I've tried?" Vance snapped. "West Coast wants shows, and they don't give a toss how they get them. In the end, all I could do was drop the highball from Baby's routine and hope that Blodwyn would leave him alone. But even that was a step too far for our new manager. We ended up having a blinding row, with me telling him that *I* was in charge of the dolphins, so he should keep his big nose out. But did he listen? No, he damn well didn't … because what he did next defied belief."

161

So far, my conversation with Vance had been decidedly one-sided – not surprising considering all he'd been through. This new manager sounded typical of the kind of go-getter attracted by this rotten industry. In fact, this rookie suit and his twisted logic reminded me very much of Backhouse – meaning he'd be right at home with the Company.

"Defied belief?" I echoed. "Why?"

"Well, next day was my day off, so officially I wasn't due in. But I happened to be passing the dolphinarium later that night and noticed that the lights were on, which was unusual, so I crept inside to investigate. Dave, I couldn't believe my eyes … There he was, standing on the stage with a whistle around his neck, a fish bucket at his feet and a presenter by his side!"

Little wonder Vance couldn't believe his eyes – this story was going from the ridiculous to the sublime.

"I had a right go at the bastard … told him he had no right trying to work the dolphins without a trainer present. But the cocky sod said that he didn't *need* a trainer, because anyone could train a dolphin."

That last remark really lit my fuse – it was like hearing Backhouse all over again.

"He said *what*? God! Sounds like another suited bum with delusions of grandeur … The pillock!"

"He then went on to tell me that *I* wasn't in charge of the dolphins … he was. He also said that he'd ordered the presenters to put Baby's highball back into the show by the next afternoon, or there'd be hell to pay. In other words, the rotten sod had overruled me."

By now, I was practically foaming at the mouth. Even after all the trauma, it seemed that the West Coast Management had learned nothing … absolutely nothing.

"I hope you gave him a piece of your mind!" I growled.

"I did – I told him what he could do with his lousy job … told him where to stick it. But, then, one of his fairground thugs grabbed me by the collar and started screaming in my face: 'Don't let the door hit your arse on the way out!' Dave, I really thought I was gonna get hammered, so I had no choice but to walk." Vance sighed. "But, now, I'm not sure if that was the right call, because, with me gone, who's left to look out for Baby?"

Who indeed? The answer to my friend's question was "no one".

"Vance, the truth is, even if you go back, there's nothing more you can do for Baby – or any of the dolphins for that matter. Management will just shout you down. West Coast is a disaster. It's always been a disaster. And it always *will* be a disaster."

Vance's silence spoke volumes. In truth, he – like me, like Gerry – had already taken that same walk … the one that led to the back door of the West Coast dolphinarium.

However, what neither of us knew at that time was just how catastrophic Blodwyn's vicious attack on Baby had actually been. This wonderful little Atlantean, who'd spent his short life in captivity only trying to please, would, in a short space of time, pay the ultimate price for Management's stupidity …

Baby would be dead … dead!

Dolphinariums … rotten, bloody dolphinariums!

⟨ 162 ⟩

It had been over a month since my ex-partner's SOS and I'd heard nothing more from him, which meant that Vance had once more disappeared from the scene. As for me, paintbrush in hand, I quickly became an integral part of Dad's signwriting business, struggling with my art in those cold, dingy garages that peppered the outskirts of my dirty old town. Yes, there was no doubt that I was now firmly back in the grasp of suburban normality. Gone was the thrill of applause; gone were the bright lights of the aqua-circus. I had a new life, and I was determined to make it work.

Since my return, Dad's business had thrived, so much so that it wasn't long before we were flogging a six-day week. Yet, despite this mountain of work, I was still finding it impossible to escape the spell of my Atlanteans. During the small hours, my mind was constantly active, trawling the dolphin radio … searching … listening for their songs – those all too familiar signatures of my two lost charges.

My unceasing fixation with the subtle wavelengths of my dolphins was not only troubling, but a telling confirmation that my burned-out psyche had now fully recovered from its past traumas, meaning that my involvement with the people of the sea was far from over.

But thankfully, my dealings with Head Office *were*! I'd received no further threats from the Company's faceless minion. It seemed that the dolphin project had relented in its quest for Herb'e's logbooks, accepting the less provocative option of letting sleeping dogs lie … little knowing that – over forty years later – the sleeper would awaken.

It had been another hard day's graft, so I decided to re-charge my batteries by giving the pub a miss and having an early night, and it wasn't long before I found myself drifting blissfully into the Land of Nod ...

Then, it happened ...

Cocooned within the Twilight Zone, I began to experience that familiar feeling of being scanned. Although faint, that telltale static which always accompanied a psychic link was unmistakeable – yet this shadow-caller was struggling to find my frequency ...

... until – a message, plain as day and minus any interference.

"David ... David ... where are you? I don't know what's happening, but I'm hurting ... Please, please ... I need you ... I'm afraid."

A diamond-tipped *connection* that could belong to no other ... Scouse!

❖ 163 ❖

The next morning, I awoke early, Scouse's plea still ringing in my ears. Although desperate to see him, I had a major problem: Dad and I had been pre-booked to letter a haulage rig that couldn't be off the road for more than twenty-four hours, making it impossible for me to respond. However, I was determined to drive to Hendle the very next day – whatever Dad's objections might be.

"You're wasting your time going to that rotten place, because you haven't a cat in hell's chance of getting in," he complained. "You're barred, for God's sake, and if you try to force your way in, you'll end up fighting with Backhouse. Besides, there's no time – we've a load of work on."

It was clear that I wasn't going to muster any support from Dad.

"Come on, gimme a break – we've *always* got a load of work on, but Scouse needs me. I should have been with him yesterday instead of lettering that rotten rig, so, today, the work will have to wait – I'm gone! As for Backhouse …"

Dad was clearly unhappy – and I could see where he was coming from. Even so, he knew better than to question my intuition, and minutes later, I was Hendle-bound – probably the last place in the world where I'd be welcome. But barred or not, I was determined to at least try to see Scouse, because, if I didn't, I'd never find any peace.

On my arrival at the safari park, I was gifted a rare stroke of good fortune: security, completely oblivious to my barring, informed me that Backhouse had left for Welby early that morning – meaning my chances of gaining access to my old pool had just increased a thousand-fold.

Furtively, I made my way to the back door of the dolphinarium, where I loitered nervously, trying to build up the courage to knock. Despite Backhouse's absence, I was still uncertain whether I'd gain entrance, especially in light of the new dolphin handler's reputation.

With a stiff upper lip, I rapped on the door, before hanging around for what seemed like an age, pensively listening for the click of a turning key. Slowly, the door half-opened, and I found myself confronted by a baleful-looking young man, whom I guessed to be Tom Darley, Hendle's head dolphin handler.

Looking at him was like seeing myself a few months earlier – pale and dishevelled, he had the troubles of the world etched across his face. He remained moodily silent, and an awkward stand-off followed, which I was the first to break.

"Hello, my name's David Capello, and many moons ago I was head trainer at this pool. I was wondering if it would be possible for me to see Scouse."

A look of shock flashed across Darley's face, but he remained stubbornly silent.

"I realise you must be very busy," I persisted, "but I've driven a long way just to see him."

I held my breath – he wasn't going to make this easy, and I realised that there was every chance he would turn me away. Suddenly, two faces appeared over his shoulder – young girls whom I assumed to be presenters.

"Look, I'm not here to make trouble. All I need is five minutes with Scouse, then I'll be on my way."

The band of three continued to wall the entrance, nervously exchanging glances. It was now touch-and-go …

Would they let me in?

❧ 164 ❧

"Did you say your name is David Capello?"

One of the girl presenters ... Thank goodness someone had finally broken the ice – now I had a chance. Pressing my advantage, I clumsily blurted a reply.

"Yes. I was explaining to your colleague that I used to be head trainer here, and I wanted to see Scouse."

Tentatively, she glanced at Darley, before ushering him aside and pushing the door fully open.

"I guess you'd better come in. Aren't you the one who trained the full somersault routine? The man they call the 'psychic trainer'?"

The "psychic trainer" – a handle that was new to me. It seemed that, since leaving the aqua-circus, I had gained quite a reputation ... but, if the look on Darley's face was anything to go by, a reputation *not* appreciated by everyone.

We continued with the small talk, although even this was strained. It was blatantly clear from his stalling tactics that the young Mr Darley didn't want me there. His behaviour was decidedly edgy, as if he had something to hide. I underwent an agonising, ten-minute interrogation before the girl presenter finally felt obliged to escort me into the pool. Darley followed, albeit begrudgingly.

Walking onto that stage was like being reborn. My nostrils instinctively pricked with the salt-laden air, which acted like a narcotic, rocketing my senses. It was hard to believe that I was actually standing on my magnificent Hendle stage again – a platform that never failed to stimulate my passion ...

My passion ...

... *she* was here, imprisoned in one of the makeshift pens on the far side of the pool. Duchess, my beautiful, beautiful Duchess ... now just another victim of Backhouse's heartless wintering policy.

Buoyed by her presence, I took a step towards the water's edge – only to have my way abruptly barred. Darley's eyes flashed a message loud and clear ... That's as far as you go! You can look, but you don't touch!

Duchess ... Had she seen me? Could she feel me? Did she know that I was here? I craned my neck to peer over his shoulder.

"You said you came to see Scouse," he snapped. "Well, he's over there ... on the walkway."

On the walkway? I threw Darley a bewildered look: how could Scouse be on the walkway?

He flapped a hand towards a mound of black tarpaulin near one of the holding pens.

"Well, you said you wanted to see him, so there he is. He died sometime last night. We don't know why, because he didn't show any signs of illness."

Scouse ... my little prizefighter ...

Dead.

How cruel could the fates be? Just over twenty-four hours earlier, my rugged Atlantean had been alive and calling to me ... and I hadn't come.

Darley barked at me aggressively.

"You don't even work here, so how did you know? How the hell did you know that something was wrong with him?"

His attitude didn't warrant an answer, but ...

"I just knew ... I *always* knew."

My blind dolphin had screamed through the blackness to the only person he could ever truly "see", the only one who'd ever cared ... the *one* who'd arrived too late.

"Well, now you know the score – Scouse is dead – so I think it's time you left. The vet will be arriving soon to perform the post-mortem, and he won't appreciate an outsider on the premises."

Darley didn't have to tell me twice – all I wanted was to get as far away from this pool as I possibly could. Scouse was gone, and Darley had already made it abundantly clear that he wasn't letting me anywhere near Duchess.

However, at that time, what I didn't know were the circumstances surrounding Scouse's death – just what that post-mortem would uncover …

… a sickening revelation that would send shockwaves throughout the captive dolphin industry.

They say that the only problem with becoming a celebrity is the unwanted attention that it brings. Something that certainly held true in my case.

As the full story of my controversial departure from the aqua-circus gathered pace, my newfound fame as the rebel "psychic trainer" seized the imaginations of those disillusioned individuals still operating within the Company ranks – graphically illustrated by an explosive and disturbing late night telephone call.

"Hello, am I speaking to David Capello? Because if I am, I have some important information for you. It concerns Scouse and his post-mortem results."

I had no idea as to the identity of this mystery caller. Nevertheless, I was determined to hear him out.

"Scouse didn't die from natural causes. He was deliberately killed – murdered!"

Instinctively, my breathing suspended.

"The post-mortem revealed that Scouse died from a foreign body lodged deep within his gut – a razor blade, to be precise – something that he'd swallowed at least twenty-four hours earlier. Please note that by using the word 'swallowed', I'm erring on the side of caution, because perhaps a more apt term should be 'was fed'."

And with that stark revelation, my anonymous caller abruptly slammed down the receiver.

I was appalled ... a razor blade, for God's sake ... a razor blade ... a paper-thin assassin that would have left Scouse screaming for death.

My blood froze as I contemplated the agonies that my little prizefighter must have suffered, and I found myself fighting the urge to vomit.

A blade … What kind of sick mind could have contemplated such a heinous act?

This news was utterly traumatizing, and galvanized my mind into overdrive in its search for answers.

Question: how could a blind dolphin have swallowed something as tiny as a blade by accident – a mini-assassin so light that it would be virtually impossible to toss into an Atlantean's mouth, even at close quarters?

Answer: he couldn't. Besides, even if – against all odds – he had managed to swallow a bare blade, it would have resulted in immediate gagging and bleeding for all to see.

Question: could Scouse have picked up the blade from the pool floor?

Answer: no – not only did Scouse have no vision, but also his bulbous nose would be far too stumpy to accomplish such a delicate task.

I could now well appreciate my faceless informant's accusation of murder, because everything – but *everything* – pointed to the blade having been concealed in Scouse's food, which meant that it had to have been fed to him deliberately by someone up-close and personal.

To my mind, there was no doubt that Scouse had been callously assassinated – a killing that bore all the trademarks of an inside job. I didn't have to be a Sherlock Holmes to deduce how the killer had gone about committing this horrible act undetected.

It would have been childishly simple. Anyone who worked – or *had* worked – in a dolphinarium knew the art of "fish loading" – an everyday practice to administer vitamins. All the killer had to do was slide the blade into the gills of a herring, thus making it invisible to any colleagues present. The feeding of this "vit-fish" would be so routine that no one would even think to question it.

It would be like *giving* candy *to* a baby.

This was a terrible revelation – a revelation that would have even the most hardened trainers whispering accusations and covertly pointing fingers, as this wouldn't be the first time they'd heard of a problematic Atlantean meeting a dubious end.

For me, this train of thought immediately rekindled the harrowing memories of yet another suspect dolphin death – the demise of Bubbles.

Although I'd always maintained that this tortured Atlantean had taken her own life, the events of the last few years had constantly raised doubts. With her mind broken by the trauma of capture and transport, Bubbles had become nothing more than a costly liability and a potential disruption to the smooth running of any commercial dolphinarium.

In many ways, she reminded me of poor Scouse, who, without Baby or me by his side, would have been considered nothing more than an expensive fish-eating machine – an Atlantean the Company accountants could well do without.

But, even more disturbing, on the morning of Scouse's death, Backhouse had inexplicably left for Welby. This prompted another glaring question: just what kind of emergency could have drawn him away from Hendle when he had a dead Atlantean lying prostrate on its walkway?

And something else was troubling me: Mr Darley. Why had Hendle's head dolphin handler been so blatantly aggressive and obstructive towards me? And why had he been so determined to keep me on stage and away from Scouse?

His actions didn't make sense – as neither did the actions of his esteemed general manager.

My mind was spawning serious allegations – so were these merely the result of bitter cynicism, or had I indeed stumbled upon something far more sinister?

Only time would tell …

Or would it?

Because knowing this business as I did, I suspected that word had already gone out to Company employees to keep tight-lipped …

… hatching yet another ignominious Industry cover-up.

❧ 166 ❧

Up at six-thirty, a hurried breakfast, then on the road for seven was all too quickly becoming the norm as Dad's signwriting business continued to flourish. That six-day week I'd so moaned about had turned into a gruelling seven, leaving me with little time for anything but work.

Since that last harrowing visit to Hendle and the distressing telephone call that followed, I'd desperately tried to put all thoughts of my lost Atlanteans behind me ... Until one day ...

"Hello, Mr Capello, remember me?"

How could I forget? This faceless individual's first call had shocked me to the core, and now it seemed he was back for more.

"You won't be surprised to hear that the Company never managed to finger anyone for that razor blade job on Scouse. There was an awful lot of 'oohing' and 'aahing', but, in the end, Scouse had always been viewed as damaged goods, so there didn't seem much point in trying *too* hard to find the culprit."

My mystery caller's cynical tone suggested that, despite his being in the loop, he had little love for the Company.

"More news that might interest you: a few weeks ago, Duchess got a name change – something that's becoming a common practice in the UK dolphinariums. It's a scam we've picked up from the Yanks ... a clever way to mask the true mortality rate of our show dolphins ... blur any unwanted tracking."

More corporate skulduggery – but I had a gnawing feeling that this telephone call wasn't just about Company misdemeanours.

"So what's this got to do with me?"

"It's got everything to do with you, Mr Capello, because with Duchess now having a new name, you probably won't be aware that she died last week. I would have called you sooner, but I thought you'd want to know the results of her post-mortem."

My princess … my princess … I didn't speak … couldn't speak …

"Turns out, the post-mortem revealed nothing. She appeared to be a perfectly healthy animal, so it's all a bit of a mystery. There are, of course, the usual theories flying around, the most logical being that she had nothing left to live for. She'd lost her partner and her trainer all in one day, and, even though the Company transported her back to Hendle, she never recovered. By all accounts, she just stopped eating, closed herself down and wasted away … died of a broken heart."

…

An abrupt click, and the line went dead.

TAIJI
DEATH COVE

❦ 167 ❧

Words … mere words. Nothing more than a callous parting shot from what I assumed to be a self-opinionated suit that got his kicks from playing games … Yet how his verbal assault had stung. In his spite, this faceless individual had ripped into my heart, inflicting a wound so deep that it would never heal.

As to his identity, I would never know or want to know – I was just grateful to see the back of him and his kind.

However, even with this tormentor gone, the dolphin grapevine provided me with one last nugget. Whispers were rife that the Company planned to close the stricken West Coast dolphinarium. A public humiliation and a costly demonstration that – despite Backhouse's claims to the contrary – *not* just "anyone with a whistle and a fish bucket" could train a dolphin. Even more gratifying, it proved just how devastating my walkout had actually been. I had to sneer: poor old Rogers … his unholy alliance with Backhouse had cost his dolphin project dearly.

Time passed, and as the months turned to years, I struggled to bury those painful memories of my time with the Company. Such a pity that the face of my despicable ex-general manager kept popping up to resurrect them.

Backhouse, ever with his eye on the main chance, had used his glib patter to promote himself as a dolphin specialist, eventually joining forces with a much-loved children's TV presenter. Together they fronted a popular animal series that propelled Backhouse to instant stardom. An ironic turn of events for a man who'd spent much of his career cruelly exploiting marine mammals.

Loved by thousands, he became such a celebrity icon that he eventually hosted his own primetime nature extravaganza – a travesty that condemned the Capello household to the annoyance of having to constantly switch TV channels.

What the public didn't know, however, was that before his much-vaunted UK TV début, Backhouse had been involved in the buying and selling of dolphins on behalf of UK dolphinariums. Media reported him to be the first buyer ever to rescue/acquire dolphins from the notorious Japanese Killing Cove — a picturesque blue-water inlet that for six months of the year quite literally drank the blood of Atlantis.

Hailed as a dolphin saviour by media and public alike, he inadvertently gave the perpetrators of this bloodbath a lucrative new outlet for their horrific trade …

… which just went to prove what I'd always maintained: animal conservation and animal exploitation are *indeed* two sides of the same coin.

❧ 168 ❧

It is man's curse to forget, and so it was with Duchess and Herb'e. My two magnificent Atlanteans had already passed into the shadow realms of marine folklore, along with their rebel trainer. The existence of my *Perfect Pair* had disappeared from the annals of the UK aqua-circus – erased by the same international conglomerate that had birthed them.

In the eyes of the public, my charges and I had quite simply ceased to exist … or so I believed.

Dad's business success had continued unabated, leaving me little time for leisure, so fearing a burnout, I decided to embark on the holiday of a lifetime to the good old USA, where I stayed with an aunt and uncle living in the Windy City.

Eager to show me off, my excited uncle raced me around as many tourist attractions as this buzzing metropolis had to offer, and it wasn't long before I found myself standing in the grounds of the city zoo, gripping a ticket for its dolphinarium – quite literally the last place in the world I wanted to be. However, not wishing to offend, I begrudgingly took my seat among the crowd of expectant tourists within the pool's auditorium.

The entire experience had a surreal feel to it – as if I didn't belong. Fidgeting nervously, I found myself fighting an overwhelming urge to jump up and run away, and it took all my willpower just to remain seated. Utterly bizarre, as to view another trainer's work as a member of an audience had once been my overriding ambition.

How wrong could I have been?

I found the whole performance deeply disturbing, and the final blow of the trainer's whistle came as a huge relief.

For me, however, the show was far from over.

It seemed that my uncle had surreptitiously tipped-off those on stage as to my identity, so any idea of a quick getaway had been well and truly scuppered.

Within minutes of the packed house emptying, I found myself surrounded by a bunch of enthusiastic dolphin handlers, all eager to take a friendly bite out of their English counterpart.

Questions … questions flew like bullets from a Gatling gun.

"Is it true that you trained the famous 'Company Dolphins' – *The Perfect Pair*?"

It was strange to hear Duchess and Herb'e referred to as the "Company Dolphins" – a brand name I deemed unworthy of my two fabulous Atlanteans.

"Are you the one they say can talk to his animals? The one they call the 'psychic trainer'?"

There it was again – that intriguing handle. Just where, oh where, had it originated? Although flattering, it was clear that the real *me* had long since been lost to this mystical twin …

Unimportant!

All that mattered was that the Company's attempts to erase the memory of my dream team had failed … and failed miserably.

"We've all heard the stories of their somersault routine … their shadow ballet. Wish we could have seen it … it must have been spectacular!"

I felt immensely proud: here in this foreign country, the magic of my *Perfect Pair* had not diminished. It pained me that the same couldn't be said of my homeland.

"How do you talk to a dolphin? How do you channel your mind to make that *connection*?"

"They say your team did everything in unison. How did you get them to perform that way? Did you teach them? Or were they a natural pair?"

Bingo! This enthusiastic presenter had just let me off the hook.

"A natural pair?" I shook my head. "No … not just a natural pair – *The Perfect Pair* …"

And so ends the story of Europe's greatest show dolphins …
Now let their legend begin …

www.theperfectpairdolphintrilogy.com

THE PLAYERS WHO HAVE LEFT
THE STAGE

Duchess: What can I say? How can I put into words how I feel? My first love ... my *true* love.

In February 1972, she was stolen, along with her partner, from the warm, inviting waters of Florida, only to be ignominiously dumped beneath the cold, slate skies of North Liston.

Yet even through the gloom of her transport box, I heard her siren song ... calling, calling ... drawing me to her like a moth to a flame. I'd never seen her like before – a young, frightened princess of Atlantis suddenly trapped in a nightmare from which she had no escape ...

... my beautiful, beautiful Duchess.

How could I resist her? She bewitched me at first sight, instantly turning my boyish curiosity into a profound and spiritual love. There and then, I made a covenant: swore that I would always stay by her side. A promise made by an innocent heart; a promise that the scheming fates ensured I would never be able to keep.

The Universe intends that each life should have a purpose, that each soul should fulfil a task. I have at last fulfilled mine: I have spoken for *all* captive Atlanteans by telling the story of my *Perfect Pair*.

"Duchess, your beauty will forever haunt me, for on the day we met, you stole my heart ... and never *gave it back. I will love you for eternity. Please, please forgive."*

Herb'e: Two Atlanteans, two *very* special Atlanteans – one already fallen victim to human captors, her liberty lost forever.

Yet *he* didn't leave her … couldn't abandon her – Herb'e, my precious, mischievous Herb'e. His selfless act of devotion on that fateful day didn't just cost him his freedom, it eventually cost him his life. His life, but not his heart, for that always belonged to *her*: *his* soulmate … *our* captivating Duchess.

On that day, no one could have guessed that here was a legend in the making: *The Perfect Pair* – an obsession that would change my life forever.

Herb'e – an adversary who would not only become my beloved friend, but also one of my very reasons for living.

"Nothing will ever heal the wounds inflicted on the day of that terrible Hendle transport – the day we BOTH lost our way. I pray that we will one day meet again amongst the stars. Love you forever. Please, please forgive."

Baby Dai: On 25th March 1972, this endearing infant was transported illegally from the US to the obscure Shire village of North Liston. Snatched at a vulnerable age from the tender care of his family, this miniature marvel spent his short life in captivity only ever trying to please. His willing disposition, along with his small size, made him an ideal candidate for somersault training, tricks at which he excelled.

Still shawled in innocence, Baby Dai harboured no dark prejudices, which helped him find happiness with the luckless Atlantean named Scouse.

In late 1974, the Universe saw fit to grant Baby his freedom – a passing that would transform his remarkable somersaults into leaps of delight.

"Enjoy a free and fruitful life in Paradise. I will always be touched by your innocence … Please, please forgive."

Scouse: On 25th March 1972, confined in the same aeroplane as his infant friend, Scouse was forced to endure a traumatic journey to the North Liston training pens – a journey that cost him his eyes. Yet, despite his catastrophic injuries, this rugged little dolphin never lost his ability to light up a room – an ironic gift to bestow on an Atlantean doomed to spend the rest of his life in darkness.

Above all others, it was *his* diamond-tipped *connection* that constantly dragged me back from the brink. So why did he have to pay such a horrific price?

"My beautiful, caring, little prizefighter, keep that inner light burning so that I may one day find you in Heaven. Your precious memory will stay with me forever ... Please, please forgive."

Smelly and Worse: Proud, defiant, some might even say "evil" – my two man-hating Ninja warriors, the unconquerable Smelly and Worse.

This formidable pair of Humboldt penguins plagued me during my time in captivity; a dastardly duo who took no prisoners, as demonstrated by the vast number of scars that decorated my arms and legs.

Nevertheless, what would I have done without them? For these aptly-named characters were an integral part of my story.

Sadly, I never knew what became of them after I left Hendle, but what I did know was that these two little birds always seemed to come out on top.

"Enjoy your new life, you little firebrands, and try not to bite your Heavenly hosts. I will never forget you."

HISTORICAL FACTS 1

Among the many morning duties of dolphinarium staff, besides the obligatory stage and auditorium clean-up, is the administration of vitamin fish, commonly referred to as 'vit-fish'. A senior member of staff, ie trainer or lead presenter, is always present when this takes place.

These vitamin tablets are easily hidden within the fish – normally a herring – a practice known as 'fish loading'. This entails pushing the tablets down the herring gills, thus making them invisible to their dolphin recipients.

It usually takes one or two fish to administer these. However, this can rise when other treatments are necessary.

Even frozen fish slowly decays, which reduces its nutritional value compared to live food. Thus, it is vital to top up the diet with supplements to keep the dolphins healthy. Nowadays, research is constantly improving the effectiveness of supplements intended specifically for dolphins. In Capello's day, however, a mix of human and animal supplements was used, as this was all that was available at the time.

On a daily basis:

- 4 x Ferrous gluconate (Iron supplement to prevent anaemia and help produce blood.)
- 1 x Gevral (Human multi-vitamin, protein and mineral supplement.)
- 4 x Dalto-col (Vitamin E supplement; anti-oxidant to help detoxify rancid oil in dead fish.)
- 3 x Vitamins (Other multi-vitamin and minerals not present in human Gevral.)

- 2 x Ascorbic acid (Vitamin C supplement – immuno booster and anti-oxidant.)
- 3 x Cytacon (Vitamin B12 supplement – essential for blood production with iron.)
- 1 x Benerva (Thiamine supplement – B1. Dead-fish produce loses Vitamin B1 very quickly, so this is essential in any all-fish diet.)

The administration of these vitamins is quite literally like *giving* candy *to* a baby.

★★★

Optional for other dolphins, but permanent for Scouse:

- Nandoral (Builds muscle; prevents oestrus in females.)

★★★

Other treatments when needed:

- Wormers/anti-parasitics (Essential for wild-caught dolphins; usually given annually in captivity. Dolphins can suffer from some very nasty worms, flukes and other exotic parasites, which can quickly build up to dangerous levels in captive pools.)
- Laxatives (To prevent blockages and help pass any foreign bodies swallowed, ie liquid paraffin, given via tube after manual capture. Also Gaviscon-type digestive aids.)
- Anti-ulcer drugs (For dolphins that develop gastritis.)

★★★

Thank you to Dr Simon JR Adams, BSc, BVMS, MRCVS for his help with this section.

HISTORICAL FACTS 2

In an effort to maintain anonymity and avoid unnecessary confusion, we have chosen to refer to Company employees and dolphinariums by the names with which our readers are familiar. Barring these name changes, this historical note is, to the best of our knowledge, an accurate account.

The Company itself was the leisure division of a well-known conglomerate, and, contrary to popular belief, it opened its first dolphinarium at Hendle Safari Park on 19th June 1972. Its first public show premièred at 12 noon 22nd June, with David Capello presenting and Vance Martin on mic, and was the first of five shows performed that day by a young Duchess and Herb'e (Flippa).

Owing to building delays, the second dolphinarium opened at the seaside resort of West Coast a few days later.

The Company opened its third pool at Welby Safari Park in early August 1973. David Capello again hosted its première show, performed by Bonnie and Clyde to a small audience of dignitaries and press. However, on that day, only three shows were performed, the remainder having to be cancelled because of water problems.

The Company had an interest in at least one other dolphinarium, but that was long after Capello had left.

The seemingly cursed West Coast dolphinarium closed its doors at the end of the 1974 summer season, only a few months after Capello's walkout. The seaside show never reopened, suggesting that the rift over Capello between West Coast and City Head Office never healed. The venue did indeed become the sacrificial lamb that the young trainer had predicted.

The Company itself ceased involvement with UK dolphinariums in 1983 because of the high mortality rate of its dolphins and the cost of replacing them.

As far as we are aware, the original dolphinarium structures remain, although none now imprisons cetaceans.

All dates and times shown in this historical account are taken from the original Flippa logbooks and are correct – although many 'official' documents state otherwise.

HISTORICAL FACTS 3

In 1985, the Department of the Environment commissioned a report into the UK captive cetacean industry. Dr M Klinowska and Dr S Brown undertook this daunting task, and published *A Review of Dolphinaria* in 1986.

Unfortunately, much of the data supplied came from the industry itself, so it comes as no surprise that the review contained inaccuracies. Whether or not this was deliberate is unclear. However, these inaccuracies could have been avoided had cetacean logbooks been archived instead of destroyed.

Capello can only speak for his own dolphins: Duchess, Herb'e, Baby, Scouse, Bubbles and Stumpy. Nevertheless, he has identified deeply troubling data that conflict with his own records, ie names of dolphins, dates of arrival, dates and places of death. Some of this information is so outrageously incorrect that he can only surmise that Dr Klinowska and Dr Brown were deliberately fed false information to cover for less palatable events.

FRIENDS OF *THE PERFECT PAIR*

We wish to say a special thank you to the following Facebook friends who work so tirelessly to make the world a better place for our beautiful cetaceans. Your unwavering support gave us the strength to finish our project.

Anita Michelle Lautsch – Activist

Anthony Tommo Thomas – Activist

April Gaye Hall – Activist and founder of the Facebook Public Group *Stand Up Against Child Abuse* (www.facebook.com/groups/264109533770298/)

Caroline Cogger – Activist and founder of the Facebook page *Granny J2* (www.facebook.com/pages/Granny-J2/605853339469853)

Darja Ribarič – Head researcher and co-founder of *Vivamar – Society for Sustainable Development for the Sea, Slovenia* and *Vivamar – Society for Marine Mammal Research and Sea Conservation, Croatia* (www.vivamar.org/en). Facebook page *Delfini in Vivamar* (www.facebook.com/vivamar), Twitter @infoVivamar

Diana Romanos – Activist and founder of *Actions4Animals* (actions4animals.com)

Frank Jones – Activist

Frederic Egersdörfer, Norma and Richard Patrick, Vickie Collins, Sharon Martin and Mia Du Plessis – Activists and co-founders of the Facebook page *Ocean Watch SA* (www.facebook.com/OceanWatchSA)

Frederic Egersdörfer – Activist and Facebook page blogger *Frederic Egersdörfer* (www.facebook.com/FreddyEgersdorfer)

Guylaine Charest – Activist

Jerusha and Bhavna Singh – Activists and founders of the Facebook page *Captivity Kills – Don't Buy a Ticket* (www.facebook.com/Captivity KillsDontBuyATicket)

June Bird Killington – Activist and founder of the Facebook page *Seaworld SHUT DOWN* (www.facebook.com/SEAWORLDSHUTDOWN)

Milda Bandzaite – Activist, artist and photographer (www.aiws.lt)

Natalie Wheatley-Mason – Activist and founder of Facebook's SDS Action Group, *Stop Dolphin Slaughter in Faroe Islands* (www.facebook.com/groups/faroewhalesanddolphins/)

Nicky Smedley – Activist and assistant admin of the Facebook page *Dolph 'N' Whale* + (www.facebook.com/DolphnWhale)

Rebecca Dennett – Activist and illustrator of *Sipke's Son – The Story of a Friesian Colt*, a book by Ruby Wooten about the Friesian horses that Rebecca worked with and loved.

Rita Evans Barnes – Activist and artist. Facebook page *Rita Evans Artist* (www.facebook.com/artistritaevans)

Shelley Anne Guinn – Activist and co-founder of the Facebook page *Swim for Freedom – Marine Mammal Advocates* (www.facebook.com/pages/Swim-for-Freedom-Marine-Mammal-Advocates/162242933918002)

Shelley Mattocks – Activist and founder of the Facebook page *Dolph 'N' Whale* + (www.facebook.com/DolphnWhale)

Tony Cook – Laird of Dunans Castle

LIST OF SHAME

When we started to write the Capello story, we were warned to expect opposition. But, as most of you know, what shocked us most was the response of the charities when we appealed to them for help.

Some turned us down flat; others expressed fear; many ignored us; but – most disappointingly – one UK charity actually took steps to discredit us.

Such is our disgust that we have compiled this list:

- Marine Connection
- Born Free Foundation
- PETA UK
- PETA USA
- Sea Shepherd UK
- Captain Paul Watson and the Sea Shepherd Organisation
- Whale and Dolphin Conservation (WDC)

A personal message from the authors of *The Perfect Pair Dolphin Trilogy*: 'The captive cetacean industry owes you all a huge debt of gratitude.'

FINAL COMMENT BY DAVID CAPELLO

Despite repeated requests, it has taken me over four decades to finally face my demons and tell the story of the two Atlanteans affectionately known as *The Perfect Pair*.

For me, recounting their tale has been a traumatic experience, resurrecting the horrors I'd tried so hard to lay to rest. So the question is: will this exposé finally exorcise my devils? The answer has to be a resounding NO. Nothing, but nothing, will ever do that.

However, this story will give the world a clear window to the truth – a direct feed through the lies and deceit perpetrated by this obscene industry. But it demands your help – a universal voice to spread its message. People need to know about the reality behind the glamour and the glitz.

The captive cetacean industry is a runaway train, with new markets springing up throughout Asia and Europe; a global industry fuelled by the vast wealth of the Russian and Eastern European oligarchs.

But this vile juggernaut can be stopped – *if* we pull together.

During their short lives in captivity, my *Perfect Pair* outshone all others, immortalising them in the eyes of an adoring public … a public who were able to pay homage for the relatively small cost of a ticket.

So the next time you wish to visit a dolphinarium (or any other facility exhibiting captive cetaceans), remember *their* story, the price *they* paid to entertain you …

… and *don't* buy that ticket!

David Capello
Ex-trainer